S.

PROJECTIVE GEOMETRY

UNIVERSITY MATHEMATICAL TEXTS

GENERAL EDITORS

ALEXANDER C. AITKEN, D.SC., F.R.S.
DANIEL E. RUTHERFORD, D.SC. DR.MATH.

PROJECTIVE GEOMETRY

BY

T. EWAN FAULKNER, M.A., Ph.D.

LECTURER IN STATISTICS AT UNIVERSITY COLLEGE, DUNDEE
IN THE UNIVERSITY OF ST. ANDREWS

OLIVER AND BOYD
EDINBURGH AND LONDON
NEW YORK : INTERSCIENCE PUBLISHERS INC.

FIRST PUBLISHED	.	.	.	1949
SECOND EDITION	.	.	.	1952
REPRINTED	.	.	.	1960

PRINTED AND PUBLISHED IN GREAT BRITAIN BY
OLIVER AND BOYD LTD., EDINBURGH

PREFACE

THE purpose of this book is to give, in as concise a form as possible, an account of the methods of Projective Geometry. Although these methods have application in space of any number of dimensions, we confine ourselves almost entirely to the geometry of the plane. In a book of this size it is not possible to give as much space as the author would wish to foundations, and many readers may well find the first chapter the most difficult. Once, however, the methods of the symbolic notation and the idea of (1-1) correspondence have been fully grasped the further development should be understood without great difficulty.

The book is intended mainly for students reading for an Honours Degree in one of our universities, but it will also serve as an introduction to more advanced and comprehensive works such as the *Principles of Geometry* by Professor H. F. Baker. It is expected that the reader will have some knowledge of the elements of both metrical and analytical geometry.

I am much indebted to Dr. D. E. Rutherford for numerous suggestions and for his continual encouragement and criticism. I have also to thank my colleague, Mrs. D. C. Pack, for help in correcting the proofs.

T. E. F.

Jan. 1948

Advantage has been taken of the printing of a Second Edition to make slight additions and also a number of corrections.

April 1952

CONTENTS

CHAPTER I

INTRODUCTION : THE PROPOSITIONS OF INCIDENCE

1. Historical note.—The study of geometry began well over two thousand years ago, and it is inevitable that in that long period there should have been several courses of development. Modern geometry is built on more than one foundation and cannot be fully appreciated without some knowledge of its history. There are three main lines of approach to the study of geometry—the metrical, the projective and the analytical—and it is important to understand the contribution which each has made to our present knowledge.

The first method of study began with the Greek geometers, and is associated with the name of Euclid. Euclidean geometry is based upon the fundamental notion of distance, or length ; distance is never defined, but is regarded as an intuitive concept which underlies every geometrical theorem. Euclidean geometry is metrical, for it assumes that every segment or angle can be measured and expressed in terms of a standard distance or standard angle.

However, in addition to theorems which were very obviously concerned with distance, geometers were interested in theorems involving the concurrency of lines or the collinearity of points. A typical example is Pappus' theorem, proved by Pappus using the methods of metrical geometry about the year A.D. 300. These projective theorems, as they were called, were for many centuries merely added to the propositions of Euclid, and were not regarded as being of a different character. Development

1

was slow, and it was not until the seventeenth century that Desargues, and to a lesser extent Pascal, established the main theorems of projective geometry. Both Desargues and Pascal made full use of the theorems of metrical geometry, and it was only after the publication of *Geometrie der Lage* by von Staudt in 1847 that projective geometry was established as a science built upon a different set of axioms from those of Euclid. It was shown that the theorems of projective geometry were independent of the concept of distance, and that distance itself could be expressed in terms of simpler projective elements. The theorems of metrical geometry were found to be special cases of the more general theorems of projective geometry, with Euclidean geometry as only part of the field covered by the science of projective geometry.

The third method of geometrical study is that known as coordinate or analytical geometry. It was introduced by Descartes, who represented a point by a set of numbers, and thus applied the methods of algebra to the solution of geometrical problems. Descartes used the idea of distance, and his geometry is thus metrical ; his achievement was that, by expressing geometrical ideas in the language of algebra, he was able to provide simple proofs of many theorems difficult to deal with by the traditional methods of metrical geometry. However, the methods of analytical geometry have not been limited in their application to metrical problems only, and since the time of Descartes, geometers such as Poncelet and Cayley have applied these methods, with modification, to the whole field of projective geometry. The Cartesian coordinates of Descartes have been replaced by homogeneous coordinates, which, since they are independent of metrical concepts, are able to deal more conveniently with projective problems.

Complex points.—The application of algebra to geometry had a very important consequence. Once the theory of complex numbers was established and it was agreed that every quadratic equation had two roots whether real or complex, it was a simple matter to deduce the existence of complex or imaginary points. Previously the problem of finding the points common to a line and a conic could not be solved satisfactorily, but, when it was known that the problem was identical with that of solving a quadratic equation, it became clear that a line and conic always had two points in common, but that these two points could be real, coincident or complex. The use of complex points opened up a very fruitful field of study, for it enabled geometers to elaborate general theorems which would not be true if the field of real points only were considered. In particular, the discovery of the " circular points " made it possible to generalise well-established theorems about circles and obtain theorems about conics through two fixed points.

2. The projective method.—The raw material of projective geometry consists of a number of elements, *points*, *lines* and *planes*. We make no attempt to define these concepts, but regard them as undefined elements related to each other according to certain axioms which we call the propositions of incidence. These axioms are not the only set of axioms upon which a logical and self-consistent geometry could be built, but they are chosen partly for their intrinsic simplicity, and partly because they provide us with a generalised geometry out of which Euclidean geometry appears as a special development.

The propositions of incidence.—In projective geometry we take a point as a completely undefined element and suppose a line to consist of an infinite set of points, and to be completely determined by any two distinct points of the set. Thus, if the line determined by the points A and B contains the points X and Y, it follows that the line determined by X and Y is the same line and contains A and B. Three or more points which belong to a line are said to be *collinear* or to lie on the line.

A plane is assumed to consist of an infinite set of points

and to be completely determined by any three distinct non-collinear points upon it. It is further assumed that a line defined by any two points of the plane lies completely in the plane. Since a plane contains an infinite number of points, not all collinear, and since any two points determine a line, it is clear that a plane also contains an infinite number of lines. It is assumed further that any two distinct lines lying in the plane have one point in common, or, expressed otherwise, a point is determined by any two of the infinite number of lines which pass through it. This last assumption forms the basis of the principle of duality in the plane which is discussed below. Lines through a point are said to be *concurrent*, and the point is called the point of intersection of the lines.

Extending, we may suppose three-dimensional space to consist of an infinite number of points and to be completely determined by any four non-coplanar points within it. A plane, and a line not lying in the plane, are assumed to have one point in common.

It follows that two planes have one line in common. For, if we take two lines in the first plane meeting the second plane in A and B, the points A and B clearly lie in both planes, and thus the line defined by A and B lies in both planes.

Since two planes have a line in common, and a third plane, which does not contain this line, meets it in one point, it follows that three planes, supposed not to have a common line, have one point in common. This result forms the basis of the principle of duality in space.

The principle of duality.—If we examine the propositions of incidence carefully we find a certain dual relationship between them. Thus, in a plane, a line is determined by two points upon it, while a point is determined by two lines which pass through it. Thus, if, by using the propositions of incidence, we are able to prove a theorem involving points and lines, then, by using similar reasoning, we should be able to prove a corresponding theorem involving lines and points. The dual theorem is obtained from the original theorem merely by the interchange of certain words, " point " and " line ", " collinear " and " concurrent ", " lie on " and " intersect in ", and so on. This is known as the principle of duality in the plane.

In space there is another form of duality. From the propositions of incidence we see that a plane is determined by three of its points, and a point is determined by three of the planes which pass through it. A line is determined, either by two of its points, or by two planes which contain it. Thus, in space, points and planes are dual elements, while a line is a self-dual element. Hence to any theorem involving points, lines and planes there corresponds the dual theorem involving planes, lines and points.

We shall have several opportunities later of illustrating the principle of duality in specific instances.

3. Desargues' theorem.—As an illustration of the propositions of incidence we prove Desargues' theorem, a theorem of very great importance in the foundations of projective geometry.

If two triangles ABC and $A'B'C'$, lying in the same or in different planes, are such that AA', BB', CC' meet in a point O ; then BC meets $B'C'$ in L, CA meets $C'A'$ in M, and AB meets $A'B'$ in N, where L, M, N are collinear.

We first consider the case when the triangles ABC and $A'B'C'$ are in different planes π and π' respectively. Since the lines BB' and CC' intersect in O, it follows that B, B', C, C' lie in a plane and BC meets $B'C'$ in a point L. Similarly CA meets $C'A'$ in M and AB meets $A'B'$ in N. The three points L, M, N evidently lie in each of the planes π and π', and are thus collinear on the line of intersection of these planes. The two triangles ABC and $A'B'C'$ are said to be in *perspective* from O.

We next consider the case when the triangles are in the same plane π. Let OPP' be any line through O not lying in π ; then, since PP' meets AA' in O, the four points P, P',

A, A' are coplanar, and PA meets $P'A'$ in a point A''. Similarly PB meets $P'B'$ in B'' and PC meets $P'C'$ in C''. The four points B, B'', C, C'' are evidently coplanar and so BC meets $B''C''$. The lines $BC, B'C', B''C''$ are the three

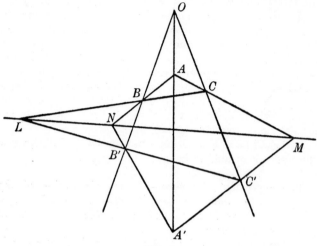

Fig. 1

lines of intersection of the three planes $PBC, P'B'C'$ and π taken in pairs, and so $BC, B'C', B''C''$ meet in a point L. Similarly $CA, C'A', C''A''$ meet in M and $AB, A'B', A''B''$ meet in N. The two triangles ABC and $A''B''C''$ lie in different planes and AA'', BB'', CC'' meet in P, and thus L, M, N are collinear. This establishes the required result.

It is important to note that in proving Desargues' theorem for the case of coplanar triangles we made use of points and lines outside the plane of the triangles. It is an interesting result that if we make no assumptions other than the propositions of incidence for the plane no proof is possible, and in fact geometries have been constructed for which the propositions of incidence for the plane hold but for which Desargues' theorem is not true.

4. The analytical method.—In the analytical approach to the study of geometry a point is represented by a set of numbers. This enables us to express elementary geometrical concepts in the language of algebra, and to solve geometrical theorems by the application of algebraic laws. In this section we give an analytical representation of the propositions of incidence and in this way provide a tool which will be of considerable use in the further development of the subject.

The symbolic notation.—We denote points by A, B, C, etc. and we let x, y, z etc. denote numbers or multipliers. We suppose that the point denoted by xA, where x is any number different from zero, represents the same point as A. The expression $xA + yB$, where x, y are not both zero, may also be taken to represent a point, and, if we suppose that x and y vary, it represents an infinite set of points, which we define as belonging to the line AB.

We suppose in what follows that the algebraic symbols obey the associative, distributive and commutative laws of algebra. For example, we assume that $xA + yB$ represents the same point as $yB + xA$; that the point $xA + yA$ can equally well be represented by $(x + y)A$ and that $xyA + xy'A$ is equivalent to $x(y + y')A$ or to $(y + y')xA$, and so on.

As we have said, the points of the line AB can be represented by $xA + yB$ where x and y vary. Any two points of the line may thus be denoted by $xA + yB$ and $x'A + y'B$; but

$$p(xA + yB) + q(x'A + y'B) = (px + qx')A + (py + qy')B,$$

and so the points $xA + yB$ and $x'A + y'B$ determine the same set of points as A and B. A line is thus determined by any two of its points, and this agrees with our original definition of a line in **2**.

If A, B, C are three collinear points, then any one point may be expressed in terms of the other two, and so we may write $-zC = xA + yB$. Thus the condition for A, B, C to be collinear is for multipliers x, y, z to exist such that

$$xA + yB + xC = 0.$$

Any three non-collinear points determine a plane, and we may denote the points of the plane defined by A, B and C by $xA + yB + zC$, where x, y, z may take all values not all zero, and so, if A, B, C, D are coplanar points

$$xA + yB + zC + tD = 0.$$

This is equivalent to the result that $-zC - tD$ and $xA + yB$ denote the same point, or that the lines AB and CD have one point in common.

Extending, we may say that the five points A, B, C, D, E lie in three-dimensional space if

$$xA + yB + zC + tD + uE = 0,$$

and thus $-tD - uE$ is equivalent to the point $xA + yB + zC$, and it follows that the plane ABC and the line DE have one point in common.

The above symbolism therefore gives us a simple algebraic representation of the propositions of incidence, and we are thus able to deal with geometrical concepts in terms of algebraic relationships.

Coordinates.—The multipliers x, y, z are sometimes referred to as coordinates, for they are numbers which define the position of some particular point. In the plane ABC the point $P = xA + yB + zC$ is said to have coordinates (x, y, z) referred to ABC as *triangle of reference*. Since the point kP with coordinates (kx, ky, kz) is the same point as $P(x, y, z)$ the coordinates are said to be *homogeneous*.

Unit point.—If the coordinates are each equal to unity we obtain the unit point. For example, the point $A + B$ or $(1, 1)$ is the unit point on the line AB, and the point $A + B + C$ or $(1, 1, 1)$ is the unit point in the plane ABC. The unit point is dependent on the coordinate system, for the coordinate system may be so defined that any arbitrary chosen point may be taken as the unit point. For example, if $P = xA + yB + zC$, we may write $A' = xA$, $B' = yB$, $C' = zC$ and $P = A' + B' + C'$. Then, referred to the triangle of reference $A'B'C'$, which is in fact identical with the triangle ABC, P is the unit point $(1, 1, 1)$. However, once the triangle of reference and the unit point are selected, the coordinate system is fixed, and any other point must be given by the general coordinates (x, y, z). It is instructive to note that the points A, B, C have coordinates $(1, 0, 0)$, $(0, 1, 0)$ and $(0, 0, 1)$ respectively, while $(0, y, z)$ represents a point of BC for all values of y, z.

Addition and multiplication of points on a line.— The fundamental processes of algebra are those of addition and multiplication. In introducing number into geometry we are therefore concerned with the geometrical counterparts of these two processes. We now obtain geometrical constructions which are equivalent to these two algebraic operations.

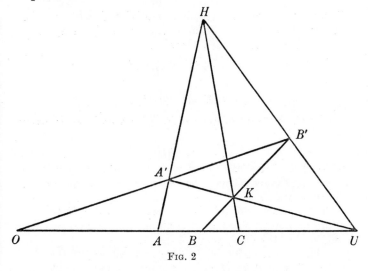

Fig. 2

Let $A = O + aU$ and $B = O + bU$ be points on the line OU. Let a line $OA'B'$ be drawn through O, and let AA' meet $B'U$ in H and BB' meet $A'U$ in K. If HK meets OU in C, the point C is defined as the *sum* of the points A and B.

To justify this definition we refer the points of the plane to OUH as triangle of reference. The point A', which lies on AH, may be expressed symbolically as a linear combination of A and H, and may be denoted by

$$A' = O + aU + hH.$$

This may be written

$$A' - O = aU + hH.$$

It follows that $A' - O$, which represents a point on $A'O$, and $aU + hH$, which represents a point on UH, are equivalent. But the point of intersection of $A'O$ and UH is B', and so

$$B' = aU + hH.$$

The point K, the intersection of $A'U$ and BB' may be expressed either as a linear combination of the symbols A' and U or of B and B': therefore

$$K = O + (a + b)U + hH,$$

or

$$K - hH = O + (a + b)U,$$

and so C, the point of intersection of HK and OU, is given by

$$C = O + (a + b)U.$$

Thus A, B, C are associated with the numbers $a, b, a + b$ respectively, and C may be regarded as the *sum* of the points A and B.

The operation of subtraction is the inverse of that of addition, and by reversing the above construction we may obtain B as the *difference* of C and A.

Again, let A and B be defined as above, and E the unit point $O + U$. Take H as an arbitrary point outside the line OU; let HE, HA meet a line through O in E', A' respectively, and HU meet $E'B$ in K. If $A'K$ meets OU in C, the point C is defined as the *product* of the points A and B.

Taking OUH as triangle of reference, the point A' may be written $A' = O + aU + hH$, and the point E', which lies on OA' and HE, may be written $E' = aO + aU + hH$.

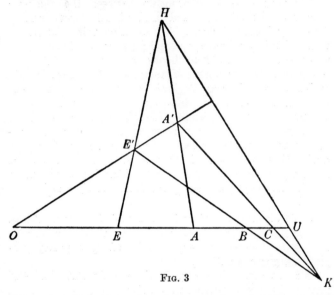

Fig. 3

The point K is the point of intersection of HU and $E'B$ and is expressed as a linear combination of the symbols E', B and H, U, and thus

$$K = (aO + aU + hH) - a(O + bU)$$
$$= (a - ab)U + hH.$$

The point C, which is the point of intersection of $A'K$ and OU, may then be written

$$C = (O + aU + hH) - \{(a - ab)U + hH\}$$
$$= O + abU.$$

The points A, B, C are thus associated with the numbers a, b, ab respectively, and C may be regarded as the *product* of the points A and B.

The inverse of multiplication is division, and by reversing the above construction we may pass from the two points A and C to their *quotient* B.

We thus have a relationship between the algebraic operations of addition and multiplication and certain geometrical constructions. To examine this relationship in detail is beyond the scope and purpose of this book, and the reader is referred to books on the Foundations of Geometry, such as Baker, *Principles of Geometry*, Vol. I, or Veblen and Young, *Projective Geometry*, for a rigorous treatment. We must, however, make one important assumption. In performing the algebraic operations of addition and multiplication we have supposed that the associative, commutative and distributive laws of algebra hold. Our assumption is that *when these operations are given a geometrical interpretation we obtain results not inconsistent with the propositions of incidence already stated.*

5. Analytical proof of Desargues' theorem.—As an illustration of the use of the symbolic notation we will prove Desargues' theorem already established by a purely projective argument in **3**.

We are given (see Fig. 1) three lines AA', BB', CC' meeting in O, and thus we may write

$$O = xA + x'A', \quad O = yB + y'B', \quad O = zC + z'C'.$$

Thus
$$yB + y'B' = zC + z'C'$$

or
$$yB - zC = z'C' - y'B'.$$

The points $yB - zC$ and $z'C' - y'B'$ are thus equivalent and BC meets $B'C'$ in L where

$$L = yB - zC.$$

Similarly $\quad M = zC - xA \quad$ and $\quad N = xA - yB.$

It follows that $\qquad L + M + N = O,$

and so L, M, N are collinear.

The above proof applies equally well whether the two triangles ABC and $A'B'C'$ are in the same or in different planes. But we stated, in **3**, that the propositions of incidence for the plane were insufficient to establish the theorem in the former case. It thus appears that the assumptions made for the symbols are more extensive and imply more than the propositions of incidence for the plane. This conclusion is further enforced by a consideration of Pappus' theorem, which we establish in the next section.

6. Pappus' theorem.—This theorem holds a position of very great importance in projective geometry. Its

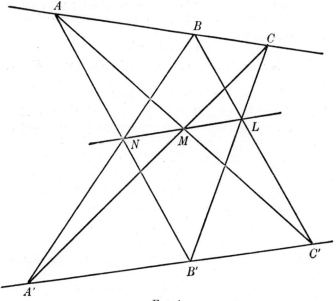

Fig. 4

significance lies in the fact that it cannot be deduced from the propositions of incidence alone, and it is thus often taken as an additional axiom of projective geometry. We establish the theorem by use of the symbolic notation, and the method of proof brings out the association of the theorem with the commutative law of multplications.

If A, B, C are any three distinct points on a line l, and A′, B′, C′ any three distinct points on a line l′, lying in the same plane as l, and if BC′ meets B′C in L ; CA′ meets C′A in M, and AB′ meets A′B in N, then the three points L, M, N are collinear.

We choose $AB'C$ as triangle of reference and express all points of the figure in terms of A, B' and C. We denote

$$M = xA + yB' + zC.$$

The point B, which lies on AC, is expressible in terms of A and C, only the ratio of the multipliers being significant : thus we may write

$$B = pxA + zC,$$

where p is some multiplier, and for A' which lies on MC we write

$$A' = xA + yB' + qzC.$$

The point C' lies on AM and $A'B'$ and can be expressed as a linear combination of the symbols for the points A and M and also of the points A' and B' ; we may thus denote

$$C' = xA + qyB' + qzC.$$

The point L is the point of intersection of BC' and $B'C$ and is thus expressible as a linear combination of the symbols for B and C' and for B' and C ; it follows that

$$L = p(xA + qyB' + qzC) - (pxA + zC)$$
$$= pqyB' + (pq - 1)zC.$$

Similarly the point N, which lies on AB' and on $A'B$, is written

$$N = (xA + yB' + qzC) - q(pxA + zC)$$
$$= (1 - qp)xA + yB'.$$

It follows that

$$L - N + (1 - pq)M = (qp - pq)xA.$$

Thus, if we assume that the symbols p and q satisfy the commutative law of multiplication $qp - pq = 0$, it follows that the right-hand side of the above identity is zero, and the three points L, M, N are collinear.   This establishes Pappus' theorem.

The association noticed above between Pappus' theorem and the commutative law of multiplication is very thoroughly discussed in Baker, *Principles of Geometry*, Vol. I, Chapter I, Section 3, and the reader is referred to this book for a detailed analysis of the place of Pappus' theorem in the logical development of projective geometry.

7. The fourth harmonic point.—Let A, B, C be three points lying on the line l.   Take any plane through l, and in this

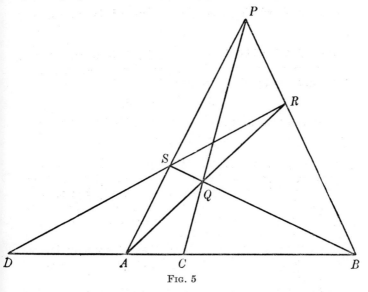

Fig. 5

plane take any lines AQR, BRP, CPQ through the points A, B, C respectively to form the triangle PQR.   Let AP meet

BQ in S, and RS meet the line AB in a fourth point D. The point D is called the *harmonic conjugate* of C with respect to A and B. It is an important theorem that the point D is unique, and is independent both of the particular plane through l and of the lines AQR, BRP, CPQ.

To prove the theorem we refer the points of the plane to the points A, B, R forming a triangle of reference. The point C lies on AB, and we write

$$C = xA + yB.$$

The point Q lies on AR, and we write

$$Q = xA + zR.$$

It follows that

$$C - Q = yB - zR,$$

and thus P, which lies both on CQ and BR, is expressible as

$$P = yB - zR.$$

The point S, which lies on BQ and AP, is expressible as a linear combination of the symbols for B and Q, and for A and P, and is therefore given by

$$S = xA - yB + zR.$$

It follows that D, which lies on RS and AB, is given by

$$D = xA - yB.$$

It is clear that if A, B and C are given, we obtain the same expression for D whatever plane we take through l, and whatever the lines AQR, BRP and CPQ may be ; thus

The fourth harmonic point is unique, and is independent of the plane in which the construction is made.

Three simple results follow :

(i) If we change the sign of y, C and D are interchanged, and thus C is the harmonic conjugate of D with respect to A and B.

(ii) Since the points $xA - yB$ and $yB - xA$ are identical, it follows that D is the harmonic conjugate of C with respect to B and A.

(iii) We further obtain, $2xA = C + D$, and $2yB = C - D$, and, since the points $2xA$ and $2yB$ are identical with A and B respectively, it follows that B is the harmonic conjugate of A with respect to C and D.

Two pairs of points, A, B and C, D, such that either pair are harmonic conjugates with respect to the other pair, are said to form a *harmonic range*, and we may denote this by writing (AB, CD) is harmonic.

Ex. 1.—O is a point in the plane of the triangle ABC; OA, OB, OC meet BC, CA, AB respectively in X, Y, Z. If X' is the harmonic conjugate of X with respect to B and C, if Y' is the harmonic conjugate of Y with respect to C and A, and if Z' is the harmonic conjugate of Z with respect to A and B, then X', Y', Z' are collinear.

Take $O = A + B + C$, then $X = B + C$ and $X' = B - C$, etc. It follows that $X' + Y' + Z' = O$.

Ex. 2.—The pair of points $A + yB$, $A + y'B$ harmonically separate the pair $A + zB$, $A + z'B$ if

$$(y + y') (z + z') = 2(yy' + zz').$$

We may write $A + yB + p(A + y'B) = (1 + p)(A + zB)$ and $A + yB - p(A + y'B) = (1 - p)(A + z'B)$, and equating the co-efficients of B, $y + py' = (1 + p)z$ and $y - py' = (1 - p)z'$. The required result follows on the elimination of p from these two equations.

The fourth harmonic line.—We have said that to any theorem involving points and lines there is a corresponding dual theorem involving lines and points. Thus, if a, b and c are three lines through L, we shall be able to construct a unique fourth line d through L which we call the harmonic conjugate of c with respect to a and b. The four lines a, b, c, d are said to form a *harmonic pencil*.

The construction for d is as follows. We take three lines p, q, r such that q and r meet on a, r and p meet on b, and p and q meet on c. We take s as the line joining the point of intersection of a and p to the point of intersection of b and q. Then d is the line joining the point of intersection

C

of r and s to L. In the figure the lines a, b, c, d, p, q, r, s correspond to the points A, B, C, D, P, Q, R, S in fig. 5, and

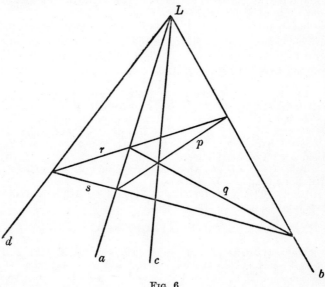

Fig. 6

the point L corresponds to the line l. To establish the uniqueness of d we may express the line c in the symbolic notation

$$c = \lambda a + \mu b,$$

where the lines are represented by a, b, c, d and the Greek letters denote multipliers, and following the steps of the previous theorem prove that

$$d = \lambda a - \mu b.$$

Ex. 3.—If $ABCD$ and $A'B'C'D'$ are two transversals of the four lines OA, OB, OC, OD, and if (AB, CD) is harmonic, then $(A'B', C'D')$ is also harmonic.

If $C = \lambda A + \mu B$ and $D = \lambda A - \mu B$, $A' = A + pO$ and $B' = B + qO$, then $C' = \lambda(A + pO) + \mu(B + qO)$ and $D' = \lambda(A + pO) - \mu(B + qO)$. The result follows.

Ex. 4.—In fig. 6, the line s meets the four lines a, b, c, d in the points of a harmonic range.

This follows by a consideration of the method of construction of a harmonic range.

Ex. 5.—Any transversal meets the four rays of a harmonic pencil in the points of a harmonic range.

This results from Ex. 3 and Ex. 4.

8. The complete quadrangle.—If we take four coplanar points P, Q, R, S, no three of which are collinear, and join them in all possible ways by six lines we obtain a complete quadrangle. Let PQ meet RS in X, PR meet QS in Y and PS meet QR in Z. Then the lines YZ, ZX, XY are called the *diagonals* and the triangle XYZ the *diagonal triangle* of the quadrangle.

Harmonic property of the complete quadrangle.— Let PQ and RS meet YZ in X_1 and X_2 respectively, PR and QS meet ZX in Y_1 and Y_2 respectively, and PS and QR meet XY in Z_1 and Z_2 respectively. It is an important result that the three ranges $(YZ, X_1 X_2)$, $(ZX, Y_1 Y_2)$ and $(XY, Z_1 Z_2)$ are harmonic. These results follow directly from the theorem in the last section. If we take $PQRS$ in fig. 5 as the quadrangle, then the points A, B, C, D are replaced by Z, Y, X_1, X_2 respectively and so $(YZ, X_1 X_2)$ is harmonic. The other two results follow similarly.

If $(YZ, X_1 X_2)$ is harmonic, the pencil of lines joining X to the four points Y, Z, X_1, X_2 is also harmonic by **7**, Ex. 5, and this is the form in which the theorem is usually stated.

The complete quadrilateral.—Dually, we may take four coplanar lines p, q, r, s, no three of which are concurrent, meeting in six points to form a complete quadrilateral. We denote the point of intersection of p and q by (pq). Let x be the line joining (pq) and (rs), y the line joining (pr) and (qs), and z the line joining (ps) and (qr). Then the three lines x, y, z form the diagonal triangle of the quadrilateral.

Ex. 1.—The vertices P, Q, R, S of a complete quadrangle may be expressed in the form $P = X + Y + Z$, $Q = -X + Y + Z$, $R = X - Y + Z$ and $S = X + Y - Z$.

Ex. 2.—The six points $X_1, X_2, Y_1, Y_2, Z_1, Z_2$ above lie in threes on four lines which form a quadrilateral with XYZ as diagonal triangle.

Ex. 3.—If A is any point on PR, and B any point on QS of a quadrangle $PQRS$, and if QA meets PB in U while SA meets RB in V, then the line UV passes through Z.

CHAPTER II

RELATED RANGES AND PENCILS: INVOLUTIONS

9. Related ranges.—Suppose we have two straight lines l and l', and let us take fixed points O and U on l, and O' and U' on l'. Then a point X of l is given by $X = O + xU$, and a point X' of l' by $X' = O' + x'U'$. We suppose that the quantities x and x' are connected by a relation of the form

$$pxx' + qx + rx' + s = 0, \qquad . \qquad . \qquad . \quad (1)$$

where p, q, r, s are constants. (We assume that this relation does not break up into linear factors; the condition for this is $ps - qr \neq 0$.) We may solve this equation either for x or for x' and obtain

$$x = -\frac{rx' + s}{px' + q}, \quad x' = -\frac{qx + s}{px + r},$$

and thus if x is assigned, x' is determined uniquely, and if x' is assigned, x is determined uniquely. There is thus a one-one algebraical correspondence between x and x', such that to any value of x there corresponds a single value of x', and to any value of x' there corresponds a single value of x. Since, however, the points X and X' are completely determined by the quantities x and x', it follows that a one-one relationship also exists between X and X'. In this case the ranges described by the points $X = O + xU$ and $X' = O + x'U'$ are said to be *related* (short for projectively related), or in (1-1) correspondence.

The lines l and l' may be distinct or coincide, but in the latter case special elements enter into the correspondence which will be discussed later. For the present we suppose that l and l' are distinct.

The fundamental equation (1), which we may notice is the most general equation giving a (1-1) algebraical relationship between x and x' depends upon the ratios of the four constants p, q, r, s. Thus, if three pairs of corresponding values of x and x' are known, the ratios of these constants can be determined as solutions of three linear homogeneous equations. It follows that a (1-1) algebraic correspondence is completely defined if three pairs of corresponding points are given. We may thus relate any three distinct points A, B, C of l to any three distinct points A', B', C' of l', but this is sufficient to establish the correspondence, and to a further point X of l there corresponds a single point X' of l', and conversely. This result is of very great importance.

One-one algebraic correspondence.—It should be stated that (1) does not define the only possible (1-1) relation between x and x'. For example, if $x = e^{x'}$, then $x' = \log x$, and, if x is real and positive and if x' is real, there is a (1-1) relation between x and x', but this relation is not algebraic. In what follows we are concerned with the properties of lines and conics, and it is shown, in **43** and **44**, that these loci are given by algebraic equations. A correspondence between two points X and X', which arises from a geometrical construction involving only lines and conics, may thus be traced out by means of a system of algebraic equations, and such a correspondence will be algebraic. Correspondences which are not algebraic may thus be excluded.

10. The cross ratio.—Suppose A, B, C, D are four points upon the line OU. We may write $A = O + aU$, $B = O + bU$, $C = O + cU$ and $D = O + dU$. The *cross ratio* of these four points is defined as the quantity

$$\frac{(a-c)(b-d)}{(a-d)(b-c)} \qquad . \qquad . \qquad . \quad (2)$$

and is denoted by (AB, CD) or $(ACBD)$.

In metrical geometry the cross ratio is expressed as $\dfrac{AC \cdot BD}{AD \cdot BC}$, but the definition given above avoids altogether the notion of distance which is not yet defined. We can see, however, that if the numbers a, b, c, d had been taken as the " distances " of A, B, C, D respectively from the fixed point O of the line AB, then the two ways of expressing the cross ratio would have been equivalent.

It is sometimes convenient to refer to the expression (2) as the cross ratio of the parameters a, b, c, d, and in this case it is denoted by $(acbd)$.

The numbers a, b, c, d which define A, B, C, D are clearly dependent upon the two base points O and U of our coordinate system, but we now show that the value of the cross ratio depends upon the four points A, B, C, D alone, and is independent of our choice of O and U.

Let O' and U' be two other points on the line OU such that

$$O' = O + pU \quad \text{and} \quad U' = O + qU.$$

Then we may express A, B, C, D in terms of O' and U':

$$a_2A = O' + a'U', \quad b_2B = O' + b'U', \quad c_2C = O' + c'U',$$
$$d_2D = O' + d'U'.$$

Thus $a_2A = (O + pU) + a'(O + qU) = (1 + a')O + (p + a'q)U$

with similar expressions for B, C and D, and comparing these with the original expressions for A, B, C, D we deduce

$$a = \frac{p + a'q}{1 + a'}, \text{ etc.}$$

and

$$a - c = \frac{(q - p)(a' - c')}{(1 + a')(1 + c')}, \text{ etc.},$$

and substituting these values in the above expression for the cross ratio it follows quite simply that

$$\frac{(a - c)(b - d)}{(a - d)(b - c)} = \frac{(a' - c')(b' - d')}{(a' - d')(b' - c')}.$$

The cross ratio is thus independent of our coordinate system and depends only on A, B, C and D.

Cross ratio of a harmonic range.—Suppose the base points O and U coincide with A and B respectively. In this case $a = 0$, $b = \infty$, and the cross ratio

$$(AB, CD) = c/d.$$

If the four points A, B, C, D form a harmonic range, we may write

$$C = A + \lambda B, \quad D = A - \lambda B.$$

The cross ratio of a harmonic range is thus

$$(AB, CD) = -1.$$

Ex. 1.—Prove that

$$(AB, \ CD) = (BA, \ DC) = (CD, \ AB) = (DC, \ BA).$$

Ex. 2.—If $(AB, CD) = k$, prove that (i) $(AB, DC) = 1/k$; (ii) $(AC, DB) = 1/(1 - k)$; (iii) $(AD, BC) = (k - 1)/k$.

Ex. 3.—If the range (AB, CD) is harmonic, prove that $(AB, CD) = (AB, DC)$.

Ex. 4.—If $(AB, CD) = (AB, DC)$, then (AB, CD) is harmonic.

Ex. 5.—If $(AB, CD) = (AC, DB) = k$, then $k = -\omega$ or $-\omega^2$, where ω is a cube root of unity. In this case the range (AB, CD) is said to be equianharmonic.

Ex. 6.—If A, B, C are three fixed collinear points, and if k is a constant, then there is one and only one point X such that $(AB, CX) = k$.

Ex. 7.—If A, B, C, D are four points on a line, then the product of the cross ratios

$$(BC, AD) \cdot (CA, BD) \cdot (AB, CD) = -1.$$

Cross ratio property of five points.—Let P, Q, R be three points on the line OU, and let us write

$$P = O + pU, \quad Q = O + qU, \quad R = O + rU,$$

and we have

$$(QR, OU) = q/r, \quad (RP, OU) = r/p, \quad (PQ, OU) = p/q.$$

Hence the product

$$(QR, OU) \cdot (RP, OU) \cdot (PQ, OU) = 1.$$

If we multiply both sides of this equation by (PR, OU),

which is the reciprocal of (RP, OU), we obtain the alternate form

$$(PQ, OU) \cdot (QR, OU) = (PR, OU),$$

a result which will be of use later.

Cross ratio of a pencil.—Corresponding to the cross ratio of four collinear points, there is the cross ratio of four concurrent lines. Let a, b, c, d be four lines of a pencil, vertex L, and let u and v be two other lines through L. Then we may write

$$a = u + \alpha v, \quad b = u + \beta v, \quad c = u + \gamma v, \quad d = u + \delta v,$$

where now the Greek letters denote coordinates. The cross ratio of the four lines is defined as the expression

$$\frac{(\alpha - \gamma)(\beta - \delta)}{(\alpha - \delta)(\beta - \gamma)}$$

and it is denoted by (ab, cd) or $L(ab, cd)$.

We may prove by a method similar to the one above that the cross ratio is independent of the particular base lines u and v chosen, and depends only on the four lines a, b, c and d.

If the four lines a, b, c, d form a harmonic pencil they may be written

$$a = u, \quad b = v, \quad c = u + \lambda v, \quad d = u - \lambda v,$$

and the cross ratio of a harmonic pencil is equal to -1.

11. Cross ratio property of a (1–1) correspondence.—In **9** we explained how a (1-1) correspondence could be established between the points $X = O + xU$ and $X' = O' + x'U'$ of two lines l and l' respectively. The correspondence was defined by the relation

$$pxx' + qx + rx' + s = 0.$$

Let the four points A', B', C', D' of the line l' correspond to the four points A, B, C, D of the line l. We shall prove the important result

$$(AB, CD) = (A'B', C'D').$$

We may write

$$A = O + aU \quad \text{and} \quad A' = O' + a'U'.$$

The points B, C, D, B', C', D' are given in a similar way by use of the quantities b, c, d, b', c', d' respectively. Then, since A and A' are corresponding points,

$$paa' + qa + ra' + s = 0$$

and

$$a = -\frac{ra' + s}{pa' + q}.$$

Similarly, we obtain equations giving b, c, d in terms of the corresponding quantities b', c', d'. It follows immediately by direct substitution for a, b, c, d in terms of a', b', c', d' that

$$\frac{(a-c)(b-d)}{(a-d)(b-c)} = \frac{(a'-c')(b'-d')}{(a'-d')(b'-c')}$$

and so the two cross ratios are equal. We have the theorem:

If two ranges are in (1-1) *correspondence, the cross ratio of any four points of the one range equals the cross ratio of the four corresponding points of the other.*

Conversely, suppose A, A'; B, B'; C, C' are three pairs of fixed points, and X and X' are variable, but such that

$$(AB, CX) = (A'B', C'X').$$

Then, if X and X' are defined by the quantities x and x', it follows directly that

$$(a-c)(b'-c')(b-x)(a'-x') = (b-c)(a'-c')(a-x)(b'-x'),$$

which may clearly be written in the form

$$pxx' + qx + rx' + s = 0.$$

Thus X and X' are in (1-1) correspondence, and since this relation is satisfied by the pairs of values $x=a$, $x'=a'$; $x=b$, $x'=b'$; $x=c$, $x'=c'$, it follows that A, A'; B, B'; C, C' are corresponding pairs in the correspondence.

We may now establish the following important result:

The cross ratio of a pencil of four lines equals the cross ratio of the range in which the pencil is cut by any transversal.

Let a transversal l cut the four rays a, b, c, d of the pencil in A, B, C, D respectively, and let L be the vertex of the pencil. We suppose that the points of l are defined by a parameter x, with A, B, C, D given by x_1, x_2, x_3, x_4 respectively, and that the lines through L are defined by a parameter x', with a, b, c, d given by x_1', x_2', x_3', x_4' respectively. It is clear that there is a (1-1) relationship between the points of l and the lines joining these points to L. There is thus a (1-1) relationship between the parameter x and the parameter x', and, by **9**, this relationship is algebraic. It follows that

$$(x_1 x_2,\, x_3 x_4) = (x_1' x_2',\, x_3' x_4'),$$

and so the cross ratio of the range of four points A, B, C, D is equal to the cross ratio of the pencil of four lines a, b, c, d. We may express this result :

$$(AB,\, CD) = L(ab,\, cd).$$

Let any other transversal cut the four lines a, b, c, d in A', B', C', D' respectively ; then, as before,

$$(A'B',\, C'D') = L(ab,\, cd),$$

and so $\qquad (AB,\, CD) = (A'B',\, C'D').$

Thus, *any pencil of four lines is cut by two transversals in ranges of equal cross ratio.*

If the lines a, b, c, d form a harmonic pencil, we deduce the result stated in **7**, Ex. 3.

Ex. 1.—A pencil of four lines is cut by two lines in ranges of equal cross ratio. (Use the alternate method of **7**, Ex. 3).

Ex. 2.—Four planes intersecting in a common line are cut by a transversal in a range of constant cross ratio.

Let us take two transversals l and l', and let d be the line of intersection of the planes. A plane through d cuts l in X and l' in X', and there clearly is a (1-1) correspondence between X and X'. Hence, taking four such planes, it follows that the cross ratio of the range cut out on l equals that of the range cut out on l'.

Notation.—The cross ratio property of related ranges suggests a convenient notation. We express the fact that

the range of points $A, B, C, \ldots$ of l is related to the range
$A', B', C', \ldots$ of l' by writing

$$l(ABC\ldots) = l'(A'B'C'\ldots),$$

or simply $(ABC\ldots) = (A'B'C'\ldots).$

Similarly, if two pencils, vertices L and L', are related, we
write

$$L(abc\ldots) = L'(a'b'c'\ldots).$$

Again, if a transversal meets the pencil of lines $a, b, c, \ldots$,
with vertex L, in the range of points $A, B, C, \ldots$ respectively, we know, by the previous theorem, that the cross
ratio of any four lines of the pencil equals the cross ratio
of the corresponding four points of the range. We may
express this by writing

$$L(abc\ldots) = (ABC\ldots).$$

12. Ranges in perspective.—Two ranges on lines l and
l' are said to be in perspective if the joins of corresponding
points are concurrent. If the point of concurrence is L,
then L is called the *centre of perspective*. Dually, two
pencils of lines are said to be in perspective if the points of
intersection of corresponding rays lie on a line. This line
is called the *axis of perspective*.

We now prove the following theorem :

*Ranges in perspective are related, with the point of intersec-
tion of the ranges as a self-corresponding point, and conversely,
related ranges with a self-corresponding point are in perspective.*

Let the ranges l and l' intersect in the point A, and let
L be the centre of perspective. Let any line through L cut
l and l' in X and X' respectively. Then there is clearly
a (1-1) correspondence between X and X', and, since the
particular line LA cuts both l and l' in A, the point A is a
self-corresponding point of the correspondence.

Conversely, we suppose that the point A of intersection
of the related ranges l and l' is a self-corresponding point.
Let B, C, D be any three other points of l, and let the
corresponding points of l' be B', C', D' respectively. Let
BB' meet CC' in L, and let LD meet l' in D''. We wish to

prove that D' and D'' coincide. Since the ranges on l and l' are related, we have

$$(AB', C'D') = (AB, CD) = k \text{ (say)}.$$

But, since the ranges $(ABCD)$ and $(A'B'C'D'')$ are in perspective from L, they are related, and

$$(AB', C'D'') = (AB, CD) = k.$$

Hence $\qquad (AB', C'D') = (AB', C'D'') = k,$

and thus, by **10**, Ex. 6, the point D'' is unique and coincides with D', and the line DD' passes through L. Similarly, the lines joining other pairs of corresponding points will pass through L, and the two ranges are in perspective.

If two ranges are in perspective from L we sometimes speak of one range as being the *projection* of the other from the point L.

Ex.—If two related ranges have a common self-corresponding point O, and if U and U' are a pair of corresponding points, then we may express any other pair of corresponding points in the form $O + xU$ and $O + xU'$.

The ranges have a self-corresponding point and are in perspective. The centre of perspective is L, a point of UU'. Taking U as unit point on the line LU' we may write $U = L + U'$, or $L = U - U'$. If P and P' are any other pair of corresponding points we may write $P = O + xU$ and $P' = O + x'U'$. Thus $P - P' = xU - x'U'$, defining the point of intersection of PP' and UU'. Thus L can be represented either by $U - U'$ or $xU - x'U'$, and consequently $x = x'$. Any pair of corresponding points are thus $O + xU$ and $O + xU'$.

We now establish the following theorem:

Any two related ranges may each be put in perspective with a third range.

For the present we prove the theorem in the case when the ranges l and l' are coplanar.

Let A, B, C be three points of the range l, and A', B', C' the corresponding points of l'. We join AA', and take L and L' as any two points upon this line. Let LB meet $L'B'$ in B_1, and LC meet $L'C'$ in C_1, and let the line B_1C_1, or l_1, meet AA' in A_1. We will show that the ranges $(ABC\ldots.)$

and $(A'B'C'\ldots)$ project from L and L' respectively into the same range on l_1. Let D be any point of the range l, and D' the corresponding point of the range l'. We let LD meet l_1 in D_1 and $L'D'$ meet l_1 in D_2. We show that D_1 and D_2 coincide. Since the ranges $(ABCD\ldots)$ and $(A_1B_1C_1D_1\ldots)$ are in perspective from L, it follows that

$$(AB, CD) = (A_1B_1, C_1D_1).$$

Similarly $\qquad (A'B', C'D') = (A_1B_1, C_1D_2).$

But, since the ranges $(ABCD\ldots)$ and $(A'B'C'D'\ldots)$ are related,

$$(AB, CD) = (A'B', C'D').$$

Therefore $\qquad (A_1B_1, C_1D_1) = (A_1B_1, C_1D_2).$

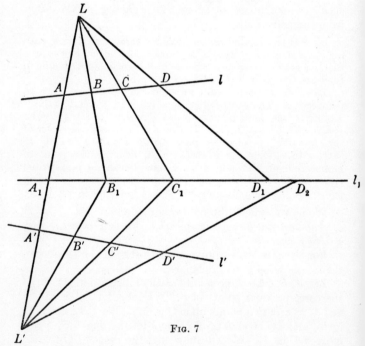

Fig. 7

The points D_1 and D_2 thus coincide, and the range on l_1 is in perspective with the ranges on l and l' from the centres of perspective L and L' respectively.

Ex.—The related ranges l and l', whether coplanar or not, may be put in perspective with a range on the line AB'.

Take L as any point of BB', and let LC meet AB' in C_1, and let $C'C_1$ meet AA' in L'. Then the points A, B, C, project from L into the points A, B', C_1, and the points A', B', C' project from L' into A, B', C_1. It is easy to show, as above, that two other corresponding points D and D' project from L and L' respectively into a point D_1 of AB'.

13. Related ranges on the same base ; double points.—In **9** it was assumed that the lines l and l' were distinct. We now consider the case when l and l' coincide, in which we have two related ranges on the same base. The points $X = O + xU$ and $X' = O + x'U$ on l are related provided x and x' satisfy the relation

$$pxx' + qx + rx' + s = 0.$$

Any point of l may be considered as belonging to either of the superimposed ranges, and a point of l is a self-corresponding point if $x = x'$ and

$$px^2 + (q + r)x + s = 0.$$

This is a quadratic equation, and there are thus two self-corresponding points, one associated with each root. These points are called *double points*, and we denote them by E and F. If the roots of the quadratic equation are equal, E and F coincide.

If the points E and F are distinct we may clearly refer all points of the line l to these points, and write $X = E + xF$ and $X' = E + x'F$. Since $x = 0$, $x' = 0$ defines E, and $x = \infty$, $x' = \infty$ defines F, we obtain $p = s = 0$, and $qx + rx' = 0$. Thus any pair of corresponding points may be simply expressed $E + xF$ and $E + kxF$, where k is the constant $-q/r$.

If the points E and F coincide, we may write two corresponding points in the form $O + xE$ and $O + x'E$, where $x' = \infty$ when $x = \infty$. It follows that $p = 0$, and, since the above quadratic has equal roots, $q + r = 0$. The fundamental relation is then $q(x - x') + s = 0$, and any pair of corresponding points are $O + xE$ and $O + (x + k)E$, where k is the constant $- s/q$.

Ex. 1.—If A, A' and B, B' are two pairs of corresponding points, then $(AB, EF) = (A'B', EF)$.

Ex. 2.—If A, A' are any pair of corresponding points, then (AA', EF) is constant. (Use Ex. 1 to prove that $(AA', EF) = (BB', EF)$.)

Ex. 3.—If there are more than two self-corresponding points, then every point is a self-corresponding point. (If E, F, G are three self-corresponding points, and X and X' a pair of corresponding points, then $(EF, GX) = (EF, GX')$, and so $X = X'$.)

The transversals of four lines in space.—As an illustration of the use of double points we prove that four non-intersecting lines in space have, in general, two transversals.

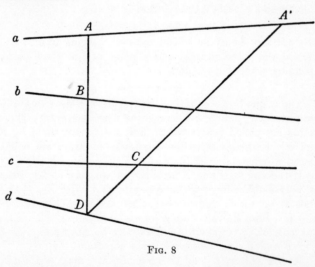

Fig. 8

Let the four lines be a, b, c, d, and let A be any point of a. There is a unique transversal ABD from A to the lines b and d, given as the line of intersection of the plane containing A and b with the plane containing A and d, and similarly there is a unique transversal DCA' from D to the lines c and a. A and A' are clearly corresponding points of related ranges, for given A, we define A' uniquely, and given A', we define A uniquely. There are two self-corresponding points A_1 and A_2, and through each of these points there is a transversal to b, c and d.

If there are more than two transversals to a, b, c, d, then, by Ex. 3 above, every point of a is a self-corresponding point, and the number of transversals to the four lines is infinite.

Ranges on the same base in perspective with a third range.—The theorem established in **12** holds for related ranges with a common base.

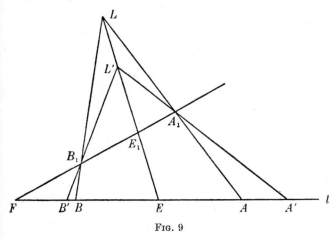

Fig. 9

Suppose A, A'; B, B' are two pairs of corresponding points of related ranges on a line l, and let the double points be E and F. Take any two points L and L' on a straight line through E. Let LA meet $L'A'$ in A_1, LB meet $L'B'$ in B_1, and LL' meet A_1B_1 in E_1. The range

D

$(A_1B_1E_1....)$ is then in perspective with the related ranges $(ABE....)$ and $(A'B'E...)$ from the centres of perspective L and L' respectively. The point of intersection of A_1B_1 with l is clearly a self-corresponding point, and so A_1B_1 meets l in the second double point F. In the case when the double points coincide the line A_1B_1 obviously passes through E.

The above is essentially a construction for the second double point of a correspondence when two pairs of corresponding points and one double point are given.

14. Related pencils.—In a plane, the dual of a range of points on a line l is a pencil of lines through a point L. If u and v are two arbitrary chosen lines through L, any other line through L is $u + \theta v$. In the same way, any line through a point L' can be expressed as $u' + \theta'v'$. The pencils with vertices L and L' are related, or in (1-1) correspondence, if θ and θ' are connected by the fundamental relation

$$p\theta\theta' + q\theta + r\theta' + s = 0.$$

To each line of the pencil, vertex L there corresponds a definite line of the pencil, vertex L' and conversely.

By a proof similar to that for ranges, we may show that the cross ratio of any four lines of the pencil vertex L, is equal to that of the corresponding four lines of the pencil vertex L'. Moreover, since we have already shown that the cross ratio of a pencil is equal to that of the range cut out on any transversal, it follows at once that *if two pencils are related, then the ranges cut out on two transversals, one for each pencil, are also related.*

Related pencils with a common vertex, double lines. —The two vertices, L and L', may coincide, and in this case corresponding lines of the related pencils may be expressed $u + \theta v$ and $u + \theta'v$. There are two lines, $u + \theta_1 v$ and $u + \theta_2 v$, where θ_1 and θ_2 are roots of

$$p\theta^2 + (q + r)\theta + s = 0,$$

which are self-corresponding. These lines are the *double lines* of the correspondence. If the roots of the quadratic equation are equal the double lines are coincident.

Related pencils of planes.—In space, the dual of a range of points is a pencil of planes all passing through a common line. Corresponding to related ranges we have related pencils of planes, and to a plane of either pencil there corresponds a unique plane of the other. We may deduce that *two related pencils of planes are cut by two transversals, one for each pencil, in two related ranges, and they are cut by two planes, one for each pencil, in two related pencils of lines.*

If the axes of the two pencils coincide we have two self-corresponding planes or *double planes*.

15. Involution on a line.—Suppose we have two related ranges on the same base l, and let E and F be the double points. Any point X of l can be regarded as belonging to either range. If it be taken as a point of the first range, the corresponding point is X', but if it be taken as a point of the second range, the corresponding point is X''. In general X' and X'' are distinct. We prove, however, that if for some point X, different from E and F, X' and X'' coincide, they do so for all positions of X. As X varies on l, the points X' and X'' clearly generate related ranges, but if X' and X'' coincide there are three self-corresponding points, E, F and X', and so, by **13**, Ex. 3, the ranges are identical. Thus any point of l, taken as belonging either to the first or to the second range, has the same corresponding point. If this is so there is said to be an *involution* on l. E and F are the double points of the involution, and pairs such as X and X' are point pairs in involution.

A fundamental property of an involution is that *any pair is harmonically separated by the double points*. The four points E, F, X and X' correspond to E, F, X' and X; thus

$$(EF, XX') = (EF, X'X),$$

and it follows, by **10**, Ex. 4, that (EF, XX') is harmonic.

The fundamental relation.—Since an involution is a particular case of a (1-1) correspondence it can be defined by the fundamental relation

$$pxx' + qx + rx' + s = 0.$$

But, if the points $X = O + xU$ and $X' = O + x'U$ are in involution, we may clearly interchange x and x' and obtain

$$px'x + qx' + rx + s = 0.$$

On subtraction

$$(q - r)(x - x') = 0.$$

The condition for an involution is thus $q = r$, since, in general $x \neq x'$.

The fundamental relation which defines an involution is thus

$$pxx' + q(x + x') + s = 0.$$

This equation contains three constants, p, q and r. The ratios of these constants can be determined if two pairs of corresponding values of x and x' are known. It follows at once that *an involution is completely determined by two of its pairs*.

The double points of the involution are obtained for $x = x'$, and correspond to those values of x for which

$$px^2 + 2qx + s = 0.$$

If the points of the range are referred to the double points E and F as base points, then the pairs $X = E + xF$ and $X' = E + x'F$ are in involution if the fundamental relation is satisfied by $x = x' = 0$ and $x = x' = \infty$. Therefore

$$p = s = 0 \quad \text{and} \quad x + x' = 0.$$

It follows that, as x varies, $E + xF$ and $E - xF$ generate involution pairs. Any pair is clearly harmonically separated by the double points, as was proved above.

Alternatively, the points of the range may be referred to some particular pair X and X' of the involution as base points. In this case, when $x = 0$, $x' = \infty$, and so $q = 0$. The fundamental relation reduces to $xx' = k$, where k is the constant $-s/p$. Any pair of the involution is $X + xX'$ and $xX + kX'$. The double points are $X + \sqrt{k}X'$ and $X - \sqrt{k}X'$, and once again it appears that any pair is harmonically separated by the double points.

Ex. 1.—Two involutions on the same base have one common pair.

Any pair of the first involution harmonically separate the double points E, F of that involution, and any pair of the second involution harmonically separate the corresponding double points E', F'. The double points of the involution determined by the pairs E, F and E', F' thus give the unique common pair of the two involutions.

Ex. 2.—There is one pair of an involution which harmonically separates a given pair of points.

Let the given points be P, Q and let E, F be the double points of the given involution; then the double points of the involution determined by P, Q and E, F belong to the given involution and harmonically separate P, Q.

Ex. 3.—A, B, C, D are four distinct points on a line. The double points of the involution determined by the pairs A, B and C, D are E, F, and the double points of the involution determined by A, C and B, D are E', F'; then $(EF, E'F')$ is harmonic.

We refer the points of the line to the base points E and F. Then $A = E + aF$, $B = E - aF$, $C = E + cF$ and $D = E - cF$. Let the involution determined by A, C and B, D be given by

$$pxx' + q(x + x') + s = 0.$$

Then

$$pac + q(a + c) + s = 0,$$

and

$$pac - q(a + c) + s = 0.$$

Since A, B, C, D are distinct, $a + c \neq 0$, and so $q = 0$ and

$$pac + s = 0.$$

The involution is then defined by $xx' - ac = 0$. The double points are $E' = E + \sqrt{ac}F$ and $F' = E - \sqrt{ac}F$, and thus E', F' harmonically separate E and F.

16. Cross ratio property of an involution.—We have shown that an involution is determined by two of its pairs. We therefore expect a single condition for three pairs of points to be in involution. This condition is contained in the following theorem :

The necessary and sufficient condition for the three pairs of points A, A' ; B, B' and C, C' to be in involution is that $(AB, CC') = (A'B', C'C)$.

This condition is obviously necessary, for the four points which correspond to A, B, C and C' are A', B', C' and C respectively, and so

$$(AB, CC') = (A'B', C'C).$$

To prove the condition sufficient, we suppose that A'' is the point which corresponds to A in the involution determined by B, B' and C, C'; then

$$(AB, CC') = (A''B', C'C),$$

and using the given condition we obtain

$$(A'B', C'C) = (A''B', C'C).$$

It follows that A'' coincides with A', and so A, A'; B, B' and C, C' are in involution.

Ex. 1.—If A, A' and B, B' are two pairs of an involution for which E and F are the double points, then A, B' ; A', B and E, F are in involution.

Ex. 2.—If $(ABCDEF) = (BCDAEF)$, then A, C and B, D are two pairs of an involution for which the double points are E and F.

Ex. 3.—If A, A' and B, B' are two pairs of points on a line, and if the points C, C' are such that (AA', BC) and $(AA', B'C')$ are harmonic, then A, A' ; B, B' and C, C' are in involution.

Ex. 4.—A, B, C are three points on a line ; A' is the harmonic conjugate of A with respect to B and C, B' the harmonic conjugate of B with respect to C and A, and C' the harmonic conjugate of C with respect to A and B ; then A, A'; B, B' and C, C' are in involution.

Ex. 5.—A range $(A_1 \, B_1 \, C_1 \dots)$ on a line l_1 is projected from U and U' respectively into the two ranges $(ABC\dots)$ and $(A'B'C'\dots)$ on the line l. The necessary and sufficient condition for these two ranges on l to be in involution is that the line UU' meets l and l_1 in two points which harmonically divide U and U'.

Ex. 6.—A, A'; B, B'; C, C' are pairs in involution on a line, and A_1, A_1'; B_1, B_1'; C_1, C_1' are their harmonic conjugates with respect to two fixed points U, V of the line. Prove that these pairs are also in involution.

17. Involution property of the complete quadrangle.

—We now establish the following theorem :

Any line meets the three pairs of sides of a complete quadrangle in three pairs of points in involution.

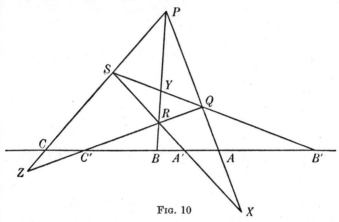

Fig. 10

Let P, Q, R, S be the vertices of a quadrangle and XYZ the diagonal triangle. Let any line l meet the three pairs of sides PQ, RS; PR, QS; PS, QR in the three pairs of points A, A'; B, B'; C, C' respectively. We prove that these pairs are in involution. We have, by projection from P on to the line QR,

$$(AB, CC') = (QR, ZC'),$$

and then, by projection from S on to the line l,

$$(QR, ZC') = (B'A', CC') = (A'B', C'C),$$

and so $\quad\quad (AB, CC') = (A'B', C'C),$

and by the theorem of the last section it follows that the three pairs of points A, A'; B, B'; C, C' are in involution.

Ex. 1.—Two coplanar triangles ABC and $A'B'C'$ are such that AA', BB', CC' meet in O ; BC, CA, AB meet $B'C', C'A', A'B'$ in L, M, N respectively, and AA', BB', CC' meet the line LMN in L', M', N' respectively ; prove that L, L' ; M, M' ; N, N' are pairs in involution. (The result follows as a property of the quadrangle $OABC$.)

Ex. 2.—P, Q, R are points on the sides BC, CA, AB respectively of a triangle ABC. Any line meets the six lines BC, CA, AB, AP, BQ, CR in L, M, N, L', M', N' respectively. Prove that the necessary and sufficient condition for AP, BQ, CR to be concurrent is that L, L'; M, M'; N, N' are pairs in involution.

Construction for the sixth point of an involution.— The above theorem enables us to construct the point C' which corresponds to any point C of an involution determined by the pairs A, A' and B, B'. The five points A, A', B, B', C are given, and we take P as any point outside the line AA'. We take any line $B'QS$ through B' to meet PA and PC in Q and S respectively, and we let PB meet SA' in R. We have now constructed the quadrangle $PQRS$, and, if QR meets AA' in C', it follows that A, A'; B, B'; C, C' are in involution.

18. An algebraic representation of an involution.— Suppose we have two pairs of points A, A' and B, B' on a line l. We may refer them to fixed base points O and U of l, and write $A = O + \alpha U$, $A' = O + \alpha' U$, $B = O + \beta U$, $B' = O + \beta' U$. Let the quadratic equation with roots α and α' be $ax^2 + 2hx + b = 0$, and the quadratic equation with roots β and β' be $a'x^2 + 2h'x + b' = 0$. We first prove that *the condition for the pair A, A' to separate the pair B, B' harmonically is $ab' + a'b - 2hh' = 0$.*

The pair A, A' harmonically separates the pair B, B' if the cross ratio

$$(AA', BB') = -1,$$

that is, if $\quad (\alpha - \beta)(\alpha' - \beta') + (\alpha - \beta')(\alpha' - \beta) = 0$

or $\qquad 2(\alpha\alpha' + \beta\beta') - (\alpha + \alpha')(\beta + \beta') = 0.$

If we now express the sum and product of the roots of the above quadratic equations in terms of the coefficients, this condition becomes

$$(ab' + a'b) - 2hh' = 0.$$

We now establish the following theorem :

The two pairs of points A, A'; B, B' *given by the quadratic equations* $ax^2 + 2hx + b = 0$, *and* $a'x^2 + 2h'x + b' = 0$ *respectively determine an involution in which any other pair is given by* $(ax^2 + 2hx + b) + \lambda(a'x^2 + 2h'x + b') = 0$, *for a suitable value of* λ.

The quadratic equation

$$(ax^2 + 2hx + b) + \lambda(a'x^2 + 2h'x + b') = 0$$

has two roots γ and γ' such that if γ is given, λ is uniquely defined, the quadratic equation given, and γ' determined as the second root. Similarly if γ' is given we derive λ and hence γ. The pair of values γ, γ' are thus associated with a single value of λ, and so corresponding to each value of λ there is a pair of points in involution. Since the particular pair A, A' are associated with $\lambda = 0$, and the pair B, B' with $\lambda = \infty$, it follows that the involution is that determined by A, A' and B, B'.

Double points.—The double points are clearly given when the equation

$$(a + \lambda a')x^2 + 2(h + \lambda h')x + (b + \lambda b') = 0$$

has equal roots, and then λ must satisfy

$$(a + \lambda a')(b + \lambda b') - (h + \lambda h')^2 = 0$$

or $\qquad (a'b' - h'^2)\lambda^2 + (a'b + ab' - 2hh')\lambda + (ab - h^2) = 0.$

We notice that the coefficient of λ is zero if the pair of points A, A' harmonically separate the pair B, B'. This enables us to deduce the following theorem :

If the double points of the involution defined by

$(ax^2 + 2hx + b) + \lambda(a'x^2 + 2h'x + b') = 0$ *are given by* $\lambda = \lambda_1$ *and* $\lambda = \lambda_2$, *and if two pairs* A, A' *and* B, B' *are given by* $\lambda = \lambda'$ *and* $\lambda = \lambda''$ *respectively, then* A, A' *harmonically divide* B, B' *if* $(\lambda'\lambda'', \lambda_1\lambda_2) = -1$.

Since the cross ratio $(\lambda'\lambda'', \lambda_1\lambda_2)$ is invariant whichever two pairs are used to define the involution, it is sufficient to prove the theorem for the case when A, A' is given by $ax^2 + 2hx + b = 0$, and B, B' is given by $a'x^2 + 2h'x + b' = 0$. In this case $\lambda' = 0$ and $\lambda'' = \infty$. Hence if $(\lambda'\lambda'', \lambda_1\lambda_2) = -1$, then $\lambda_1 + \lambda_2 = 0$, and so

$$ab' + a'b - 2hh' = 0,$$

and in consequence the pair A, A' harmonically separates the pair B, B'.

Ex. 1.—The fundamental equation which determines the involution is

$$(ah' - a'h)xx' + \tfrac{1}{2}(ab' - a'b)(x + x') + (hb' - h'b) = 0.$$

Ex. 2.—The double points of the involution are given by

$$(ah' - a'h)x^2 + (ab' - a'b)x + (hb' - h'b) = 0.$$

Ex. 3.—If the points of the range are referred to the double points as base points, the involution is given by $(ax^2 + b) + \lambda(a'x^2 + b') = 0$, and if the points of the range are referred to some particular pair of the involution as base points it is given by $(ax^2 + 2hx + b) + 2\lambda x = 0$.

Ex. 4.—A, A' ; B, B' ; C, C' ; D, D' are four fixed pairs in involution ; H is a variable point in the base ; P, Q, R, S are the harmonic conjugates of H with respect to the four fixed pairs ; prove that the cross ratio (PQ, RS) is constant.

In the notation of the present section, the involution pairs are associated with a parameter λ, the four fixed pairs being given by $\lambda_1, \lambda_2, \lambda_3, \lambda_4$, while the harmonic conjugates of H with respect to the involution pairs are given by parameter k, with P, Q, R, S given by k_1, k_2, k_3, k_4 respectively. It is easy to see that there is a (1-1) correspondence between λ and k, and so $(k_1 k_2, k_3 k_4) = (\lambda_1 \lambda_2, \lambda_3 \lambda_4)$.

Ex. 5.—If $\lambda_1, \lambda_2, \lambda_3, \lambda_4$ are the parameters associated with the four pairs A, A' ; B, B' ; C, C' ; D, D' of an involution, then $(\lambda_1 \lambda_2, \lambda_3 \lambda_4) = (AB, CD) \cdot (A'B', CD)$.

19. Pencils in involution.—In the plane, the dual of a range of pairs of points in involution is a pencil of pairs of lines in involution. Corresponding to the double points of the range are the double lines of the pencil, and we have the important property that every pair of lines of the involution pencil is harmonically separated by the double lines. Since a transversal cuts a harmonic pencil in a harmonic range, it is evident that any line cuts the pairs of lines of an involution pencil in a range of pairs of points in involution, and that the intersections with the double lines are the double points of the range.

An important example of a pencil of lines in involution is that of pairs of perpendicular lines. This involution possesses many interesting properties, but, as we have not yet given the projective definition of perpendicularity, we must leave a consideration of these properties till a later section.

The dual of the theorem established in **17** may be stated as follows :

The four lines of a complete quadrilateral will meet in three pairs of points ; these three pairs, if joined to any arbitrary point L of the plane, will form pairs of lines in involution.

This result enables us to construct the line c' which corresponds to the particular line c in the involution determined by the two line pairs a, a' and b, b'.

CHAPTER III

THE CONIC

20. Introduction.—In this chapter we obtain some of the elementary properties of the conic. Conics, or conic sections, were studied early in the history of mathematics as the sections of a right circular cone. They were later defined by the well-known focus-directrix property, and it was shown, in the notation of coordinate geometry, that a conic could be represented by the general equation of the second degree connecting the two coordinates x and y of a point P. It followed immediately that a line, given by the general linear equation, and lying in the same plane as the conic, was met by the conic in two points. In projective geometry we define a conic by means of related pencils of lines, but it may be shown, when certain metrical ideas are introduced, that the curve defined in this way possesses the focus-directrix property.

We assume, unless otherwise stated, that all the elements considered in this chapter lie in a plane.

21. Projective definition of the conic.—We define a conic as the locus of the points of intersection of corresponding rays of two related pencils of lines. Beginning with this definition we first prove the fundamental result, mentioned above, that a conic is met by a line in two points.

Let A and B be the vertices of the two pencils, and let l be any line. The line l cuts the two related pencils in two related ranges ; these ranges have two self-corresponding points, and these points are points of intersection of corresponding rays of the two pencils. The line l thus meets the conic in two points.

One ray of the pencil vertex B passes through A, and this meets the corresponding ray of the pencil vertex A in A. The conic therefore passes through A and similarly through B.

A line through A meets the conic in the points A and P; the lines AP and BP are corresponding lines of the pencils vertices A and B respectively. When the point P coincides with A, the line AP is defined as the *tangent* at A, and BP becomes BA. The tangent at A is thus the line of the pencil vertex A which corresponds to the line BA of the pencil vertex B. Similarly the tangent at B is the line of the pencil vertex B which corresponds to the line AB of the pencil vertex A.

Degenerate case.—A special case arises when the pencils are so related that the ray AB of the pencil vertex A corresponds to the ray BA of the pencil vertex B. In this case let two pairs of corresponding rays be AP, BP and AQ, BQ, and let PQ meet AB in R. The related pencils vertices A and B cut the line PQ in related ranges, and these related ranges have three self-corresponding points P, Q, and R. It follows, by **13**, Ex. 3, that every point of PQ is a self-corresponding point. Every point of PQ is thus a point of intersection of corresponding rays of two related pencils, and the conic therefore contains the line PQ. Again, if we join any point of the line AB to the points A and B we also get a pair of corresponding rays, and so the conic contains the line AB. The conic therefore degenerates into a pair of lines.

A curve of order two is a conic.—A curve which is met by a general line in two points is said to be of *order* two; we have shown that a conic is of order two, and we now show, conversely, that *every curve of order two is a conic*.

Let A and B be two points on a curve of order two. A line through A meets the curve in a unique point P, and to the ray AP there corresponds the unique ray BP; P is thus the point of intersection of corresponding rays of two related pencils, and the curve is a conic.

Five points determine a conic.—Let us take five points A, B, C, D, E, no four of which are collinear, and consider pencils with vertices A and B. Two related pencils are completely defined if three pairs of corresponding rays are given. We take, then, rays BC, BD, BE as corresponding to the rays AC, AD, AE respectively, and the locus of the point of intersection of corresponding rays of the related pencils vertices A and B is then a conic through the five given points.

Six points A, B, C, D, E, F do not, in general, lie on a conic; if they do so the rays AC, AD, AE, AF of a pencil vertex A correspond to the rays BC, BD, BE, BF respectively of the related pencil vertex B. We have therefore

$$A(CDEF) = B(CDEF).$$

If we now take C, D, E, F to be fixed points, and A and B two positions of a variable point of the conic, this result may be expressed as follows:

The cross ratio of the four lines which join four fixed points of a conic to a variable point of the conic is constant.

22. Related ranges on a conic.—We will now define related ranges on a conic. Let A be a fixed point of the conic, and l a fixed line which we suppose does not pass through A. A line through A meets the conic in a further point P and l in a point P'. There is clearly a (1-1) relationship between P and P'. Thus, to a range of points P' on l, there corresponds a range of points P on the conic.

Extending, we may take two related ranges on l and, corresponding to them, two related ranges on the conic. If P and Q are corresponding points of these two related ranges, and if P varies on the conic, Q also varies, but the pencil of lines AP is related to the pencil of lines AQ. If three positions of P, and the corresponding positions of Q, are given, the related ranges are completely defined.

Thus far we have defined related ranges by reference to some fixed point A of the conic, but, by the last theorem of **21**, as P varies on the conic, the pencil of lines AP is related to the pencil of lines BP, where B is any other point of the conic. Similarly, the pencil of lines AQ is related to the pencil of lines BQ. Thus, *if two ranges of points upon a conic are related, the pencils obtained by joining the points of these ranges to any point of the conic are also related.*

Ex.—A, B, C are three fixed points. Show that there are in general two triangles PQR whose sides QR, RP, PQ pass through A, B, C respectively and whose vertices are on a fixed conic.

Let a line through A meet the conic in Q and R, and let BR and CQ meet the conic again in P and P' respectively. There is clearly a (1-1) correspondence between P and P', and P and P' generate related ranges with two double points. There is one triangle associated with each of these double points.

23. Involution on a conic.—Two ranges of points on a conic are in involution if the pencils formed by joining the points of these ranges to any other point of the conic are in involution.

We will now prove the theorem:

Chords of a conic drawn from a fixed point T cut the conic in pairs of points in involution.

Let A be a fixed point on the conic, and let any chord through T cut the conic in the points P and P'. To the line AP there corresponds the unique line AP', and to AP' there corresponds AP. The lines AP and AP' are thus a pair in involution. There are two double rays of the involution AX and AY, and the lines TX and TY are clearly tangents to the conic from T, and since no involution can have more than two double rays, these are the only tangents which can be drawn from T to the conic.

We now prove the converse theorem:

Every involution on a conic is given by chords through a fixed point.

Let P, P' and Q, Q' be two pairs of the given involution, and let the lines PP' and QQ' meet in T. Then P, P' and Q, Q' are pairs of the involution cut out on the conic by chords through T, but, since an involution is completely determined by two of its pairs, it follows that this involution must coincide with the given involution.

Ex. 1.—P and P' are a pair in involution on a conic, and X and Y are the double points. If A is any other point of the conic, prove that $A(PP', XY)$ is harmonic.

Ex. 2.—Two chords PP' and QQ' of a conic meet in T; AS is the tangent at a point A of the conic; prove that AP, AP'; AQ, AQ'; AT, AS are pairs in involution.

24. The conic as an envelope.—In the projective geometry of the plane the dual of a point is a line, and the dual of a locus of points is an *envelope* of lines. Points which satisfy some given condition form a locus, and lines which satisfy a given condition form an envelope. We have defined a conic as a locus of points; in this section we show that it may also be regarded as an envelope of lines.

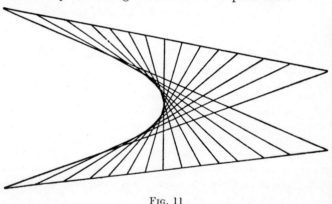

Fig. 11

A conic, or, as we will now call it, a point-conic is the locus of the meet of corresponding rays of two related

pencils. Dually, we define a line-conic as the envelope of
the join of corresponding points of two related ranges on
different bases. We have shown that a point-conic is met
by any line in two points, and every curve possessing this
property is a point-conic. It follows, dually, that a line-
conic has two of its lines through any point, and every
envelope possessing this property is a line-conic.

At every point of a point-conic there is a tangent line,
defined as in **21**, and associated with the point-conic,
considered as a locus, there is the envelope of the tangent
lines. Dually, on every line of a line-conic there is a point
which we call the point of contact with the line-conic, and
thus associated with a line-conic there is a locus of points.
A point-conic is thus both a locus and an envelope, and
dually, a line-conic is both an envelope and a locus.

It is an important theorem that *the tangents of a point-
conic are the lines of a line-conic, and dually, the points of
contact of a line-conic are the points of a point-conic.* This
result follows immediately, for we have shown in **23** that
there are two tangents to a point-conic through any point,
and these tangents are therefore the lines of a line-conic.
Both the point-conic and the line-conic are thus self-dual
figures, and in future will be referred to simply as conics.

Ex. 1.—What is the dual of the degenerate case of **21** ?

Ex. 2.—Prove directly that a line-conic is completely
determined by five of its lines.

A cross-ratio property.—Let A be a fixed point of a
conic, and t a fixed tangent. Let P be a variable point of
the conic, and let the tangent at P meet t in P'. There is
a (1-1) relationship between the lines AP through A, and
the points P' of t; for any line through A meets the conic
in one further point P, and the tangent at P meets t in a
unique point P'; and conversely, from a point P' of t there
is one tangent to the locus, other than t, meeting it in P,
and thus a unique line AP. It follows that the cross ratio
of the pencil of four lines which join A to any four points
of the conic is equal to the cross ratio of the range of four

E

points in which the tangents at these four points meet t. We proved in **21** that the cross ratio of this pencil was independent of the point A, and it follows, dually, that the cross ratio of the four points is independent of t. We therefore have the theorem :

The cross ratio of the pencil of four lines which join four fixed points of a conic to any other point of the conic is constant and equal to the cross ratio of the range cut out on any tangent to the conic by the tangents at the four fixed points.

25. Desargues' theorem.—Let A, B, C, D be four fixed points, no three of which are collinear, and let l be a given line. By the theorem proved in **21** there is a unique conic through A, B, C, D and a fifth point P of l. This conic meets l again in a point P'. As we vary P on l we get a (1-1) relationship between P and P'. Since exactly the same conic is defined by the five points A, B, C, D, P' as by the five points A, B, C, D, P it follows that P and P' are pairs in involution. This establishes the theorem of Desargues which we may express as follows :

A system of conics through four fixed points is met by any line in pairs of points in involution.

Three of the conics through A, B, C, D are degenerate and consist of the line-pairs AB, CD ; AC, BD ; AD, BC. The line l meets these three line-pairs in three point-pairs which are included in the above involution. We thus obtain the involution property of the complete quadrangle already established in **17**.

The involution established on l has two double points, and so there are two conics of the system which touch l. We thus have the theorem :

There are two conics through four points which touch a given line.

If l passes through one of the diagonal points of the quadrangle, this point is a double point of the involution on l, and only one non-degenerate conic touches l.

As a particular case we may take l as one of the three

diagonals of the quadrangle $ABCD$; the double points of the involution are the extremities of this diagonal, and divide all pairs of the involution harmonically; hence :

The diagonals of a complete quadrangle cut any conic which circumscribes the quadrangle in pairs of points harmonically separated by the extremities of the diagonals.

The dual of Desargues' theorem. — Desargues' theorem is concerned with conics through four fixed points. There is a dual theorem relating to conics which touch four lines. This dual theorem was originally due to Sturm. It may be stated as follows :

The pairs of tangents from any point to a system of conics which touch four fixed lines form pairs of lines in involution.

Included among the conics through four fixed points are three line-pairs; dually, included among the conics touching four fixed lines are three point-pairs forming the three pairs of opposite vertices of the complete quadrilateral defined by the four lines. These point-pairs determine pairs of the involution, and we have the result :

The three pairs of lines which join any point to the three pairs of opposite vertices of a complete quadrilateral form three pairs of lines in involution.

Ex. 1.—Prove that there are two conics which pass through a fixed point and touch four fixed lines.

Ex. 2.—Prove that there are two conics which pass through a fixed point and touch three lines, one at a fixed point.

Ex. 3.—A, B, C are three fixed points, and l is a line on which there is an involution. Show that all conics through A, B, C and a pair of points of the involution also pass through another fixed point D.

26. Pascal's theorem.—We now make use of Desargues' theorem to establish a celebrated and important theorem due to Pascal :

If a hexagon is inscribed in a conic, the points of inter-section of opposite sides are collinear.

Let $ABCDEF$ be a hexagon inscribed in a conic; let BC meet EF in M; CD meet AF in N, and let the line

MN meet AB and DE in L and L' respectively. It is necessary to prove that L and L' coincide. Let MN meet the conic in the pair of points P and P', and CF in R.

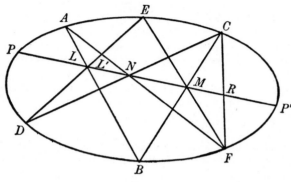

Fig. 12

The conic is one of the system of conics which pass through the vertices of the quadrangle $CDEF$, and if we apply Desargues' theorem for the line MN, it follows that the three pairs of points PP', MN and RL' are in involution. Similarly, if we consider the quadrangle $ABCF$ and again apply Desargues' theorem, it follows that the three pairs PP', MN and RL are in involution. These two involutions have in common the pairs PP' and MN, and must therefore coincide. The points L and L', both of which correspond to R in the involution, thus coincide. The opposite sides AB and DE of the hexagon therefore meet on MN, the line joining the meets of the other two pairs of opposite sides.

If the conic degenerates into a pair of lines and A, C, E lie on one line, while B, D, F lie on the other, we obtain Pappus' theorem, already established in **6**.

The converse theorem that, *if the points of intersection of opposite sides of a hexagon are collinear, then the six vertices lie on a conic*, is also true, and may be proved very easily by a *reductio ad absurdum* method.

Construction of points on a conic.—This converse theorem provides us with a very simple construction for obtaining other points on a conic, five of whose points are known.

Suppose we are given five points A, B, C, D, E and any line EF through E. We will determine the point F where this line meets the conic through A, B, C, D, E. Let AB meet DE in L, BC meet EF in M and let CD meet LM in N; then AN meets EF in the required point F, for L, M, N, the points of intersection of opposite sides of the hexagon $ABCDEF$, are collinear. By choosing a series of lines through E, we can in this manner obtain any number of points of the conic.

Brianchon's theorem.—Pascal's theorem is concerned with six points on a conic ; there is a dual theorem relating to six tangents to a conic. This theorem may be stated as follows :

If the six sides of a hexagon are tangents to a conic, then the three lines which join opposite vertices are concurrent.

There are many special cases of both Pascal's theorem and its dual which arise when certain of the six points or six tangents coincide. For example, suppose that the six vertices of the hexagon $ABCDEF$ coincide in pairs, A with B, C with D and E with F. The lines AB, CD and EF are then the tangents at A, C and E respectively. We immediately derive the result that the tangents at the vertices of a triangle inscribed in a conic meet the opposite sides in points which are collinear. Other special theorems are obtained in a similar manner.

Ex. 1.—Construct the tangent at any one of five given points on a conic.

Ex. 2.—Construct the point of contact of any one of five given tangents to a conic.

Ex. 3.—If a quadrangle is inscribed in a conic, prove that the tangents at its vertices meet in pairs on the sides of the diagonal triangle.

Ex. 4.—If a triangle is circumscribed to a conic, prove that the lines joining the vertices to the points of contact with the opposite sides are concurrent.

Ex. 5.—If a quadrilateral is circumscribed to a conic, prove that the lines joining the points of contact of opposite sides intersect at one of the vertices of the diagonal triangle of the quadrilateral.

27. Pole and Polar.—The polar of a point X with respect to a conic may be defined as the locus of the harmonic conjugate of X with respect to the pair of points in which a variable line through X cuts the conic. We first prove that the polar is a line.

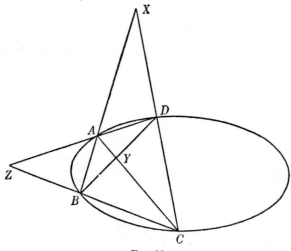

Fig. 13

Let X be any point and let AB and CD be two chords of the given conic through X; let AC meet BD in Y and AD meet BC in Z. We will prove that the polar of X with respect to the conic is the line YZ.

A chord through X cuts conics through the four points A, B, C, D in pairs of points in involution, and, since one of these conics consists of the lines AB and CD, it follows that X is a double point of the involution. The other double point is the harmonic conjugate X' of X with respect to the pair of points in which the chord cuts the given conic. Since the chord also cuts the line pair AC, BD in a pair of the involution, it follows that the line YX' is the harmonic conjugate of YX with respect to the lines YA and YB. The locus of X', which defines the polar of X, is thus a line through Y. Similarly, the polar of X may be shown to pass through Z, and so must be the line YZ. The point X is called the *pole* of YZ.

Let the polar of X meet the conic in T and T'; T is then the harmonic conjugate of X with respect to the points of intersection of XT with the conic, and since one of these is T, these two points of intersection coincide, and XT is a tangent. *The polar is thus the chord of contact of tangents from X to the conic.* Since any line meets the conic in two points and the tangents at these two points meet in a fixed point, it follows that *the pole of a given line is unique.*

In the special case when X is on the conic the polar is the tangent at X.

The points X, Y, Z form the diagonal triangle of the quadrangle $ABCD$, and thus Y and Z depend only on the four points A, B, C and D. The point X has therefore a unique polar with respect to all conics through A, B, C and D. Similarly the polars of Y and Z with respect to all these conics are the lines ZX and XY respectively. The triangle XYZ thus possesses the property that each side is the polar of the opposite vertex with respect to any conic through A, B, C and D. It is called a *self-polar triangle*. This result may be expressed as follows:

The diagonal triangle of a quadrangle is a self-polar triangle with respect to all conics which circumscribe the quadrangle.

Pole and polar for a degenerate conic.—We have assumed above that the conic was non-degenerate. We now suppose that the conic degenerates into the pair of lines YA and YB. The polar of a point X is evidently the line YZ which harmonically separates YX with respect to the lines YA and YB. The pole of YZ is not however unique, for any other point on YX would clearly have YZ as its polar.

A special case arises when X coincides with Y, the point of intersection of the line pair. In this case a line through X meets the conic in two points coincident with Y, and the harmonic conjugate of X with respect to these points is undefined. Any line of the plane may thus be arbitrarily chosen as the polar of X.

For the rest of this section we will assume the conic to be non-degenerate.

Elementary properties of pole and polar.—Let Q be any point on the polar of P, and let PQ meet the conic in the pair of points R and S. Since Q lies on the polar of P, the range (PQ, RS) is harmonic, and consequently P is a point on the polar of Q. We thus have the simple but important result that, *if the polar of P passes through Q, then the polar of Q passes through P.*

Points P and Q which are such that the polar of each passes through the other are called *conjugate points*.

The above theorem may be expressed somewhat differently that, *if the pole of a line p lies on a line q, then the pole of q lies on p.*

Lines such as p and q are called *conjugate lines*.

We now deduce the result that, *if $P, Q, R, S \dots$ are collinear points, then their polars with respect to a conic are concurrent.* Let P, Q, R, S lie on a line l, and let L be the pole of l, then, since l, the polar of L, passes through P, the polar of P passes through L. A similar result holds for the polars of $Q, R, S \dots$ The polars of all the points $P, Q, R, S \dots$ are therefore concurrent in L.

It is a further theorem that *the range $(PQRS \dots)$ is related to the pencil, vertex L, formed by the polars of $P, Q, R,*

$S\ldots$ Let $p, q, r, s\ldots$ be the polars of $P, Q, R, S\ldots$ Corresponding to any point P of l there is a unique polar, p, passing through L, and corresponding to any line, p, through L, there is a unique pole, P, lying on l. There is thus a (1-1) relationship between the points of l, and the lines through L; so that

$$l(PQRS\ldots) = L(pqrs\ldots).$$

Let AB and CD be two conjugate chords of a conic meeting in R. The tangents at A and B meet in T, the pole of AB, which is on CD. The points A and B are double points of the involution determined by chords through T. Thus, if P be any point upon the conic, PC, PD are a pair in an involution pencil with PA, PB as double lines, and so $P(AB, CD)$ is harmonic. Thus *the pencil formed by joining the extremities of conjugate chords to any point of the conic is harmonic.*

By reversing the steps of the above argument we easily obtain the converse theorem that, *if the pencil obtained by joining the extremities of two chords of a conic to any point of the conic is harmonic, then the chords are conjugate chords.*

Duality of pole and polar.—We have defined the polar of a point with respect to a conic and have shown that it is a line. Dually, if we take a line p, and a variable point Q upon it, then the line which is the harmonic conjugate of p with respect to the pair of tangents from Q to the conic passes through a fixed point P. We show that the line p and the point P are in the relationship of polar and pole.

If we take as a special position of Q one of the points of intersection of p with the conic, then the line which is the harmonic conjugate of p with respect to the tangents from Q, which coincide, is the tangent at Q. The point P is thus the meet of the tangents at the points of intersection of p with the conic, and so p and P are polar and pole.

There is therefore a dual relationship between pole and polar, and to every theorem concerning points and their polars with respect to a conic there is a corresponding dual theorem relating to lines and their poles.

For example, we know from the definition of pole and polar that the line joining two conjugate points with respect to a conic is harmonically separated by its intersections with the conic, and dually we have the result that *two conjugate lines meeting in a point are harmonically separated by the tangents from that point to the conic.*

A self-polar triangle is a self-dual figure. The theorem relating to conics circumscribing a quadrangle, established earlier in this section, thus has as its dual :

The diagonal triangle of a quadrilateral is a self-polar triangle with respect to all conics which are inscribed to the quadrilateral.

Ex. 1.—Show that the pole of the line AB is the meet of the polars of A and B.

Ex. 2.—TX and TY are the tangents from a point T to a conic, and A is any other point on the conic ; AX, AY meet a line through T in P and Q respectively ; show that P and Q are conjugate points with respect to the conic.

Ex. 3.—A and B are conjugate points with respect to a conic, and M is a point on the conic ; AM, BM meet the conic in C and D respectively. Prove that AB and CD are conjugate lines, and that AD and BC meet on the conic.

Ex. 4.—Prove that all conics which pass through a fixed point and have a fixed triangle as self-polar triangle pass through three other fixed points.

Ex. 5.—Prove that the locus of the point of intersection of lines, one through each of two fixed points A and B, which are conjugate with respect to a given conic, is a conic which passes through A and B, and through the points of intersection of the polars of A and B with the given conic.

Ex. 6.—Show that on any line pairs of conjugate points with respect to a conic form pairs in involution, and the double points of the involution are the points of intersection of the line and the conic.

Ex. 7.—Show that the envelope of the polars of points which lie on a given conic with respect to another given conic is a third conic. (There are two of these polars through any point.)

Ex. 8.—State the duals of the theorems of Examples 6 and 7.

28. Properties of two conics.—A line meets a conic in two points, and a line-pair meets a conic in four points. Since a line-pair is a degenerate conic it is reasonable to suppose that two conics meet in four points. This is proved later, in **44**, but for the present the result is assumed.

Two conics thus have four common points, and dually two conics have four common tangents. When one of the conics degenerates into a point-pair, the common tangents are the two pairs of tangents from these points to the conic.

Two conics therefore define a quadrangle, formed by the common points, and a quadrilateral, formed by the common tangents. It is an important property that the diagonal triangle of the quadrangle is also the diagonal triangle of the quadrilateral.

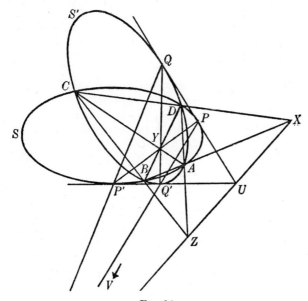

Fig. 14

Let two conics S and S' meet in the four points A, B, C, D and let XYZ be the diagonal triangle of the quadrangle $ABCD$. Let PQ be a common tangent of S and S' touching S at P and S' at Q, and let it meet XZ in U. Let UP' be the other tangent from U to S. Since U lies on XZ, the polar of Y, it follows that PP' passes through Y, and, since UX and UY are conjugate lines, the line UP' is the harmonic conjugate of UP with respect to UX and UY. Similarly, the tangent UQ', from U to S' is the harmonic conjugate of UQ with respect to UX and UY, and so $UP'Q'$ is a common tangent of the two conics. Two common tangents to S and S' thus meet in a point U of XZ, and similarly, the other two common tangents also meet on XZ. The line XZ is thus one side of the diagonal triangle of the quadrilateral formed by the four common tangents, and in the same way we may show that YZ and XY are the other sides of the triangle ; hence :

The diagonal triangle of the quadrilateral formed by the four common tangents of two conics is also the diagonal triangle of the quadrangle formed by their four common points.

Conics and triangles.—Let S and S' be two conics such that there is a triangle ABC inscribed in S, and self-polar with respect to S'. We prove that there are an infinite number of triangles which possess this property.

Let A' be any point on S, and let the polar of A' with regard to S' meet S in B' and C'. The triangle $A'B'C'$ is clearly inscribed in S, and we show that it is also self-polar with respect to S'. Let $B'C'$ meet S' in P and Q, and let $B'C'$ meet BC and AA' in X and X' respectively.

The pole of the line AA' with regard to S' is the point X, the meet of the polars of A and A', and therefore X and X' are conjugate points with regard to S', and so X, X' divide P, Q harmonically. Similarly, if $B'C'$ meets CA and $A'B$ in Y and Y' respectively, and meets AB and $A'C$ in Z and Z' respectively, the pairs of points Y, Y' and Z, Z' also divide PQ harmonically. P and Q are thus the double

points of the involution which contains the pairs X, X';
Y, Y' and Z, Z', but this involution is that determined on
the line $B'C'$ by conics through the four points A, B, C, A',

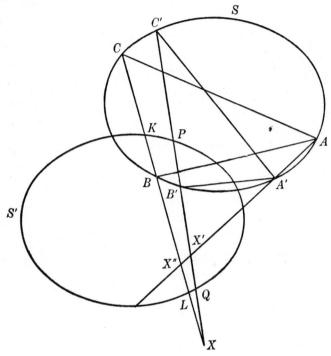

Fig. 15

and since S is one of these conics, it follows that B' and C'
harmonically divide P and Q. The polar of B' with regard
to S' therefore passes through C', and is, in fact, the line
$A'C'$. Similarly the polar of C' is the line $A'B'$. The triangle $A'B'C'$ is thus self-polar with respect to S'. Since we
may derive a triangle such as $A'B'C'$ starting with any
point A' of the conic, we deduce the theorem:

If two conics are such that there is a triangle inscribed in one and self-polar with respect to the other, then there are an infinite number of such triangles.

The above theorem can be expressed in a somewhat different form :

If two triangles are self-polar with respect to a conic, then their six vertices lie on a conic, and conversely, *if two triangles are inscribed in a conic, then there exists a conic with respect to which both triangles are self-polar.*

Let the triangles ABC and $A'B'C'$ be self-polar with respect to a conic S'. Then, according to the above argument, B' and C' are a pair of the involution determined on the line $B'C'$ by conics through A, B, C and A'. A conic through the five points A, B, C, A', B', therefore passes through C'.

To establish the converse theorem, we take ABC and $A'B'C'$ as two triangles inscribed in a conic S. Let $B'C'$ meet BC and AA' in X and X' respectively, and let BC meet AA' in X''. Let P and Q be the double points of the involution determined by the pairs B', C', and X, X', and K and L the double points of the involution determined by the pairs B, C and X, X''. We take a conic S' passing through the four points P, Q, K, L and touching AK at K, and we prove that the triangles ABC and $A'B'C'$ are self-polar with respect to S'. Since the ranges (XX', PQ) and (XX'', KL) are harmonic, it follows that $X'X''$ is the polar of X with regard to S'. The polars of X and K with regard to S' thus pass through A, and so XK, or BC, is the polar of A. Further, since (BC, KL) is harmonic, B and C are conjugate points with regard to S', and it follows that ABC is a self-polar triangle with respect to S'. Again, since $(B'C', PQ)$ is harmonic, B' and C' are conjugate points with regard to S', and, if we take A'' as the pole of $B'C'$ with regard to S', then $A''B'C'$ is a self-polar triangle with respect to S'. The line $B'C'$ passes through X, and so A'' lies on AA', the polar of X, but, since both triangles ABC and $A''B'C'$ are self-polar with respect to S', their vertices must lie on a conic through A, B, C, B', C' and this conic is S. The point A'', which lies on both AA' and S, must therefore coincide with A'. The two triangles ABC and $A'B'C'$ are thus self-polar with respect to S'. It is clear that S' is the only conic which fulfils the requirements.

The duals of the preceding theorems may be stated as follows :

If two conics are such that there is a triangle circumscribed to one and self-polar with respect to the other, then there are an infinite number of such triangles ; and

If two triangles are self-polar with respect to a conic, then their six sides touch a conic; and conversely, *if two triangles are circumscribed to a conic, then there exists a conic with respect to which both triangles are self-polar.*

By combining the theorems now established we obtain :

If two triangles are inscribed in a conic, then their six sides touch a conic, and conversely, *if two triangles are circumscribed to a conic, then their six vertices lie on a conic ;*
and then we readily deduce

If two conics are such that there is a triangle inscribed in one and circumscribed to the other, then there are an infinite number of such triangles.

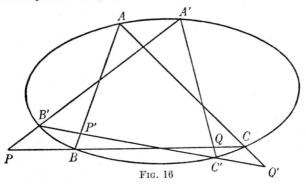

Fig. 16

This last theorem is of sufficient interest and importance to merit a direct proof, which we now give.

Let ABC and $A'B'C'$ be two triangles inscribed in a conic ; let BC cut $A'B'$ and $A'C'$ in P and Q respectively, and let $B'C'$ cut AB and AC in P' and Q' respectively. By considering the pencils from A and A' we have

$$A'(BCPQ) = A'(BCB'C')$$
and $$A(P'Q'B'C') = A(BCB'C') ;$$

but since the points A, B, C, A', B', C' lie on a conic,

$$A(BCB'C') = A'(BCB'C'),$$
and so $$(BCPQ) = (P'Q'B'C').$$

Therefore the cross ratios of the two ranges in which the lines BC and $B'C'$ meet the lines $AB, AC, A'B', A'C'$ are equal, and this is the condition that $AB, AC, A'B', A'C'$, $BC, B'C'$ should touch a conic.

The dual of this theorem is its converse.

Ex.—Two conics S and S' intersect in the points K, L, M, N. If the tangent at K to S' intersects S again in a point the tangent at which touches S' at another point, prove that similar properties hold for the points L, M, N.

29. Pencils of conics.—A conic is completely determined by five points, and the system of conics through four points A, B, C and D is called a pencil. The points A, B, C, D are the base-points of the pencil. There is one conic of a pencil through a fixed point, and in this respect, as in others, a pencil of conics is analogous to a pencil of lines.

If two conics of a pencil are given, then the four base-points are defined, and so a pencil is completely determined by any two of its conics.

There are three pairs of lines through four points, and so *in every pencil there are three line-pairs.* By Desargues' theorem the conics of a pencil determine an involution on a line l, and there are two conics of the pencil which touch l.

Dually, we have conics touching four fixed lines, no three of which are concurrent. Such conics are said to form a *line-pencil*, and one member of the pencil touches any fifth line, and two members pass through a fixed point. The four fixed lines are the *base-lines* of the pencil.

Pencils are specialised if two or more of the base-points coincide. For example, there is a pencil of conics which passes through two fixed points A and B and touches a given line l at C. In this case C and D coincide, but the line l is regarded as the line CD. Dually, we can have a line-pencil, where each conic touches two fixed lines, and touches a third fixed line at a fixed point.

Double contact.—As a further special case we may suppose that A and B coincide, and also C and D. The lines AB and CD, which we may denote by t and t', are then tangents to all conics of the pencil, and the pencil consists of conics touching the lines t and t' at the fixed points A and C. A pencil of conics of this type is said to have double contact. One of the line pairs consists of the lines t and t', and the other two line pairs coincide, and consist of the line AC, taken twice.

Any line l meets conics of the pencil in involution pairs, but one of the double points of the involution is the point where AC meets l. Thus, of the two conics which touch l, only one is non-degenerate, and the other consists of the line AC, taken twice.

Since the duals of a point and its tangent are a tangent and its point of contact, it is evident that conics with double contact form a self-dual figure.

Polar of a point with regard to conics of a pencil.—Let us consider a pencil of conics through A, B, C and D, and let X be any point. We will prove that the polars of X with regard to the conics of the pencil are concurrent.

Let S be the unique conic of the pencil through X, and let x be the tangent to S at X. By Desargues' theorem, conics of the pencil meet x in pairs of points in involution, and X is one of the double points. Let Y be the other double point, and let S' be any other conic of the pencil. S' meets x in the points P and P' which form a pair of the

F

involution. The range (XY, PP') is thus harmonic, and as a consequence the polar of X with regard to S' passes through Y. It is clear that the polars of X with regard to all conics of the system pass through Y, and we have the result that *the polars of a point with regard to the conics of a pencil are concurrent.*

The points X and Y are conjugate points with respect to all conics of the pencil and the polars of Y with respect to the conics of the pencil pass through X.

Dually, we obtain the result that *the poles of a line with respect to the conics of a line-pencil are collinear.*

Pole of a line with regard to conics of a pencil.— Let us take a pencil of conics through the four points $A, B, C, D,$ and let XYZ be the diagonal triangle of the quadrangle $ABCD$. If l is any line we will show that the poles of l with regard to the conics of the pencil lie on a conic.

There are two conics of the pencil which touch l; let the points of contact be I and J. Any conic S of the pencil meets l in P and P' such that the range (PP', IJ) is harmonic. Let the pole of l with regard to the conic S be T. Then the polar of I with regard to S passes through J and T and is the line JT, and similarly the polar of J is IT. Therefore TIJ is a self-polar triangle with respect to S. We thus have two triangles XYZ and TIJ, both self-polar with respect to S, and it follows, by **28**, that the point T lies on the conic S' through X, Y, Z, I, J; hence:

The locus of the poles of a line with regard to the conics of a pencil is a conic.

The eleven-point conic.— By taking particular conics of the pencil and the poles of l with regard to these conics we obtain particular points of S'. For example the points I and J arise as the poles of l with regard to the conics of the pencil which touch l. Again, as proved on page 56, the points X, Y, Z may be regarded as the poles of l with respect to the three line pairs of the pencil. We now show how six other points of S' may be obtained.

Let l meet the six lines AB, CD, AC, BD, AD, BC in the points L, L', M, M', N, N' respectively. Let L_1 be the harmonic conjugate of L with respect to A and B, and let

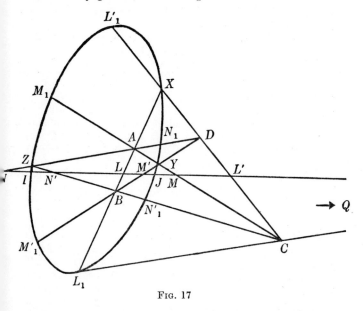

Fig. 17

the points L_1', M_1, M_1', N_1, N_1' be defined in a similar manner. We prove that the six points L_1, L_1', M_1, M_1', N_1, N_1' lie on S'.

Let CL_1 meet l in Q and let R be the harmonic conjugate of C with respect to Q and L_1. There is one conic of the pencil through R. The polar of L_1 with regard to this conic passes through Q since (L_1Q, RC) is harmonic, and it passes through L since (L_1L, AB) is harmonic. Therefore, with regard to this particular conic, the polar of L_1 is l. The point L_1 thus lies on S'. In a similar manner we may show that the points L_1', M_1, M_1', N_1, N_1' also lie on S'.

The conic S' is thus a conic through the eleven points

$I, J, X, Y, Z, L_1, L_1', M_1, M_1', N_1, N_1'$, and it is referred to as the *eleven-point* conic associated with the quadrangle $ABCD$ and the line l.

Ex. 1.—What is the dual of the theorem of the eleven-point conic ?

Ex. 2.—What is the eleven-point conic associated with a pencil of conics with double contact ?

Ex. 3.—Prove that if the three sides QR, RP, PQ of a variable triangle PQR pass through fixed points A, B, C respectively, and P lies on a fixed conic through B and C, and Q lies on a fixed conic through C and A, then R lies on a fixed conic through A and B.

Ex. 4.—A variable line is taken through a fixed point O to meet the sides of a triangle ABC in X, Y, Z, and U is the harmonic conjugate of X with respect to Y, Z. Prove that the locus of U is a conic through O, A, B, C.

Ex. 5.—If, in Example 4, OA cuts BC in L, and L' is the harmonic conjugate of L with respect to B, C, prove that the tangents at A and O are AL' and OL' respectively.

Ex. 6.—A, B, C, D are the points of intersection of two conics S and S' ; Q, Q' are fixed points on S and S' respectively; a variable chord through A meets S and S' in P and P' respectively ; prove that the locus of the meet of PQ and $P'Q'$ is a conic through Q, Q', B, C, D.

Ex. 7.—A and B are fixed points and P, Q variable points of a conic such that the cross ratio (AB, PQ) is constant. Prove that AP and BQ intersect on a fixed conic having double contact with the given conic at A and B.

Ex. 8.—A line joining a fixed point O to a variable point P of a given conic meets the polar of O in X, and Q is taken on OX so that the cross ratio (OX, PQ) is constant. Prove that the locus of Q is a conic which has double contact with the given conic at its points of intersection with the polar of O.

Ex. 9.—A, B, C, D are four points on a conic. Prove that the quadrangle $ABCD$ and the quadrilateral formed by the tangents at A, B, C, D have the same diagonal triangle.

Ex. 10.—PQ and $P'Q'$ are variable chords of a conic meeting in a fixed point O, and such that PP' passes through a fixed point X; prove that QQ' passes through a fixed point which lies on OX.

Ex. 11.—A variable conic of a pencil through the four

points A, B, C, D meets a fixed conic through A and B further in P and Q. Prove that PQ passes through a fixed point on the line CD.

Ex. 12.—A variable triangle PQR is inscribed in a conic, and the sides QR, RP, pass through fixed points A, B. Show that if A and B are conjugate with regard to the conic then PQ passes through a fixed point C.

CHAPTER IV

ABSOLUTE ELEMENTS : THE CIRCLE : FOCI OF CONICS

30. Introduction.—The Euclidean space to which we are accustomed in elementary geometry has certain properties different from those of the projective space we have been considering. In projective space two lines have always one point in common, but in the Euclidean space we make a distinction between lines which meet and lines which do not meet or are parallel. We can eliminate this distinction by supposing that Euclidean space be extended to include certain inaccessible points or points at infinity, and it then possesses the fundamental property that any two lines have one point in common, but the common point of two parallel lines is at infinity. Any line is supposed to contain an infinite number of finite points, but only one point at infinity, and this is in agreement with the well-known result of Euclidean geometry, that through a given point there is one line parallel to a given line, namely, the line joining the point to the point at infinity on the line. The points at infinity within a given plane are supposed to lie on a line, called the line at infinity, and so parallel lines meet at a point on the line at infinity.

A further important property of Euclidean space is that which permits us to speak of the distance between two points or the angle between two lines. Euclidean geometry is metrical in that it supposes that every segment and angle can be measured.

Thus, if we are to obtain Euclidean geometry as a modification of projective geometry, we have first to intro-

70

duce the idea of parallelism, and then we have to provide a suitable definition of distance and angle. In the present chapter we are concerned mainly with the first of these modifications, but it will also be convenient to define perpendicularity. In a later chapter we shall give a projective definition of distance and angle.*

31. Absolute elements.—Let us choose an arbitrary line in the projective plane, which we call the *absolute line* of the plane, and take two arbitrary points I, J upon it, which we call the *absolute points*. If we identify the projective plane with the Euclidean plane the absolute line is the line at infinity, and the absolute points the so-called circular points at infinity, but for the present we may regard these absolute elements as entirely arbitrary. Under these conditions the terms, which we will now define, parallel, perpendicular, mid-point, circle, etc., represent concepts more general than those these terms would represent in elementary geometry.

Two lines which meet on the absolute line are said to be *parallel*, and there is clearly one line through a given point of the plane parallel to a given line. Again, if the line AB meets the absolute line in D, and if C is the harmonic conjugate of D with respect to A and B, then C is said to be the *mid-point* of AB.

Two lines are said to be *perpendicular* if they meet the absolute line in two points which are harmonic conjugates with respect to the absolute points I and J. Thus, through a given point, not on the absolute line, there is only one line perpendicular to a given line. Again, lines which pass through the absolute points are *self-perpendicular*. The pairs of points on the absolute line which are harmonic conjugates with respect to the absolute points form pairs in involution and the double points of the involution are the absolute points; hence:

* Cf. Appendix to McCrea: *Analytical Geometry of Three Dimensions.*

Pairs of perpendicular lines through a point form pairs of lines in involution, and the double lines are the lines joining the point to the absolute points.

Ex. 1.—The line joining the mid-points of two sides of a triangle is parallel to the third side.

Ex. 2.—The lines joining the vertices of a triangle to the mid-points of the opposite sides are concurrent. The point of concurrence is the *centroid*.

32. The circle.—Any conic which passes through both the absolute points is called a *circle*. Since there is one conic through five points, there is one circle through three points other than the absolute points, and if these three points are collinear the circle degenerates into a line together with the absolute line.

The pole of the absolute line is the *centre* of the circle, and any chord through the centre is a *diameter*. Since any line through the centre meets the circle in points which are harmonic conjugates with respect to the centre and the point of intersection of the line with the absolute line, it follows that the centre is the mid-point of every diameter.

Properties of circles.—Many of the well-known properties of circles arise very simply from the above definition.

Let C be the centre of a circle, and DD' a diameter. Since C is the pole of the absolute line, DD' and IJ are conjugate chords, and if P is any point on the circle $P(DD', IJ)$ is harmonic. The lines PD and PD' are thus perpendicular and, in the language of Euclidean geometry, *the angle of a semicircle is a right angle.*

Let a chord PQ of a circle meet the absolute line in R; the mid-point M of the chord is the harmonic conjugate of R with respect to P and Q; the line CM is the polar of R with respect to the circle, and so, if CM meets the absolute line in S, then (RS, IJ) is harmonic. The lines MS and MR are thus perpendicular, and we have the theorem that *the line joining the centre of a circle to the mid-point of a chord is perpendicular to the chord.* The centre of the circle through three points A, B, C thus lies on the perpendicular bisectors of the sides of the triangle ABC and is called the *circumcentre*.

As a particular case of the previous result a tangent is perpendicular to the diameter through its point of contact. If the tangents to the circle at P and Q meet in T, then T lies on the polar of R, i.e. on CM, and so the line joining the point T to the centre passes through the mid-point of its chord of contact and is perpendicular to it.

Orthogonal circles.—Since two conics intersect in four points, two circles have two common points other than I and J. Let these common points be P and Q. Let the tangents to one circle at P and Q meet in T, then T lies on the line perpendicular to PQ through its mid-point, but this line passes through the centres of both circles, and so T lies on the line of centres. Let us suppose that the tangents to both circles at P are perpendicular. We prove that the tangents at Q are also perpendicular. The tangent to the first circle at P is a diameter of the second and passes through its centre, but, since the tangents at P and Q meet on the line of centres, the tangents to the first circle at P and Q meet at the centre of the second. The tangent to the first circle at Q is thus a diameter of the second, and so the tangents to the circles at Q are perpendicular. Circles possessing the property that the tangents at each of the common points are perpendicular are said to be *orthogonal*.

If DD' be a diameter of a circle, then any pair of points R, S which harmonically separate D, D' are said to be *inverse points* with respect to the circle. We now establish the following theorem :

If two circles are orthogonal, then any diameter of one meets the other in a pair of inverse points, and, conversely, *if one circle passes through a pair of inverse points of the other, the two circles are orthogonal.*

Let a diameter DD' of one circle meet the other in R and S ; let P be one of the common points of the circles, and let p be the tangent to the circle PRS at P. The pencil of circles touching p at P meets the line RS in pairs of points in involution. We show that D and D' are the double points of this involution. The tangents at P and D to the circle PDD' are perpendicular to p and DD' respectively, and if they meet in N, then N is the centre of a circle touching p and DD' at P and D respectively. This circle therefore

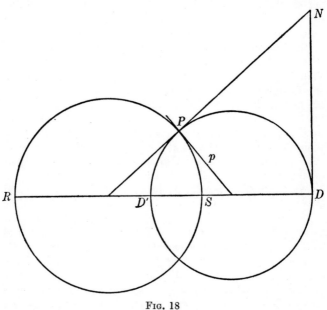

Fig. 18

belongs to the pencil defined above, and D is a double point of the involution on DD'. A similar argument shows that D' is the other double point. Therefore, since R, S is one pair of the involution, R, S harmonically separate D, D', and R, S are inverse points with respect to the circle with DD' as diameter.

To prove the converse theorem we suppose that P is a

point common to the two circles, and we notice that there is a unique circle through R and P which is orthogonal to the circle PDD'. This circle passes through S, the harmonic conjugate of R with respect to D and D', and so must be the given circle through R and S. The two circles are thus orthogonal.

Coaxal circles.—Two circles meet in two points other than the absolute points and the system of circles through

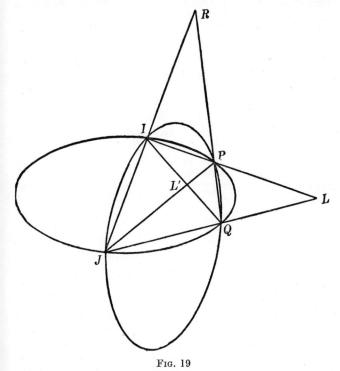

Fig. 19

these two points form a pencil. Such a system is called a *coaxal system*, and there is one circle of the system through any third point. If P, Q are the common points, the line PQ is called the *radical axis* of the system. If PI meets QJ in L and PJ meets QI in L', L and L' are the *limiting points* of the system. If PQ meets IJ in R, the triangle $LL'R$ is the diagonal triangle of the complete quadrangle $IJPQ$, and, by **27**, is self-polar with respect to all conics through I, J, P and Q, that is, with respect to all circles of the coaxal system. Since IJ passes through R, the pole of LL', it follows that the poles of the line IJ with respect to all circles of the system lie on LL'. Hence, *the centres of all circles of a coaxal system lie on a line passing through the limiting points.* Again, since LL' and PQ meet IJ in points which are harmonically conjugate with respect to I and J, it follows that *the line of centres and the radical axis are perpendicular.*

By the harmonic theory of the complete quadrangle, the line LL' meets the lines PQ and IJ in points which harmonically separate L and L'. Thus N, the point of intersection of PQ and LL' is the mid-point of LL'. Since PQ is perpendicular to LL', all circles through L and L' have their centres on PQ. These circles form a coaxal system, and since P and Q are the points of intersection of $LI, L'J$ and $LJ, L'I$ respectively, the limiting points of this system are P and Q.

We thus have two systems of coaxal circles, one through P and Q, and the other through L and L', such that the radical axis of either system is the line of centres of the other, and the limiting points of either system are the common points of the other. It is an important property that any two of these circles, one taken from each system, are orthogonal. This follows, because LL' meets any circle through P and Q in points which harmonically separate L and L', and so L and L' are inverse points with respect to this circle.

Concentric circles.—Circles with a common centre are said to be *concentric*. If C is the common centre, they form a pencil, having double contact with CI and CJ at I and J respectively. They are a special case of a coaxal system where the radical axis is the absolute line. With suitable choice of absolute line any system of conics with double contact may be regarded as a system of concentric circles.

The Euler line of a triangle.—Let the absolute line IJ meet the sides BC, CA, AB of a triangle ABC in A_1, B_1, C_1 respectively, and let A_1, A_1'; B_1, B_1'; C_1, C_1' be pairs of the involution having I, J as double points. If AA_1', BB_1', CC_1' meet BC, CA, AB in A'', B'', C'' respectively, the lines AA'', BB'', CC'' are perpendicular to the sides BC, CA, AB respectively. If AA'' meets BB'' in H, the four points A, B, C, H define a complete quadrangle, and two pairs of opposite sides BC, AH and CA, BH meet IJ in the involution pairs A_1, A_1'; B_1, B_1' respectively. It follows, by **17**, that the third pair of opposite sides AB, CH meets IJ in a third pair of the involution, namely, C_1, C_1'. The line CH thus passes through C'', and the three lines AA'', BB'', CC'' are concurrent. The point H is called the *orthocentre* of the triangle ABC.

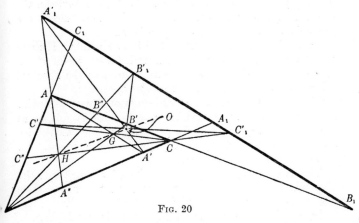

F̲ɪɢ. 20

Let A', B', C' be the mid-points of BC, CA, AB respectively; the perpendicular bisectors of the sides of the triangle ABC are then $A'A_1', B'B_1', C'C_1'$, and these lines are also perpendicular to $B'C'$, $C'A'$, $A'B'$ respectively, and thus concur in O, the orthocentre of the triangle $A'B'C'$. The point O is the circumcentre of the triangle ABC.

The centroid, G, of the triangle ABC is, by **31**, Ex. 2, the point of concurrence of AA', BB' and CC'.

To prove that O, G, H are collinear, we notice that the two triangles $AA'A_1'$ and $BB'B_1'$ are such that AB, $A'B'$, $A_1'B_1'$ concur in C_1, and so, by Desargues' theorem, the points of intersection of corresponding sides, namely O, G, H, are collinear. The line OG is called the *Euler line* of the triangle ABC.

33. The conic and the absolute points.

In Euclidean geometry we make a distinction between three types of conics : the ellipse, which has no real points at infinity ; the parabola, with two coincident points at infinity ; and the hyperbola, with two real but distinct points at infinity. As we have, as yet, made no distinction between real and imaginary points, we are unable to distinguish between the ellipse and the hyperbola. We can, however, define the parabola and the rectangular hyperbola.

All conics meet the absolute line in two points. If these points are coincident the conic is called a *parabola*, and if they are harmonic conjugates with respect to the absolute points the conic is called a *rectangular hyperbola*.

The tangents to a conic at its points of intersection with the absolute line are called the *asymptotes*. It follows at once that the asymptotes of a parabola are coincident with the absolute line, and the asymptotes of a rectangular hyperbola are perpendicular.

The absolute line meets the conics of a pencil in pairs of points in involution. The involution has two double points, and so, in any pencil of conics there are two parabolas. Included in the involution there is, by **15**, Ex. 2, one pair which harmonically separates I and J, and so, in any pencil there is, in general, one rectangular hyperbola.

34. Central properties of conics ; conjugate diameters.—The *centre* of a conic is the pole of the absolute line. For the parabola, the centre lies on the absolute line. A chord through the centre is a *diameter*, and it is clear that, except in the case of the parabola, the centre is the mid-point of every diameter. Since the centre of a parabola is on the absolute line, all diameters of a parabola are parallel.

Conjugate lines through the centre of a conic are called *conjugate diameters*. If d and d' are conjugate diameters, their poles, D and D', are the points of intersection of the absolute line with d' and d respectively. Chords through D are parallel to d', and have their mid-points on d. Thus we have the theorem :

The locus of the mid-points of chords of a conic parallel to a diameter is the conjugate diameter.

The tangents at the points of intersection of d with the conic clearly pass through D, the pole of d, and since D lies on d' at its point of intersection with the absolute line, the tangents at the extremities of a diameter are parallel to the conjugate diameter.

Since the asymptotes are the tangents to a conic from its centre, it follows, by one of the results of **27**, that they harmonically divide each pair of conjugate diameters. Pairs of conjugate diameters with respect to a conic are therefore pairs of lines in involution, and the asymptotes are the double lines of the involution.

Ex. 1.—Prove that conjugate diameters of a circle are perpendicular.

Ex. 2.—Prove that a conic has, in general, one pair of perpendicular conjugate diameters, and any conic with more than one such pair is a circle.

Ex. 3.—PP' is a diameter of a conic and Q any point on the curve ; prove that PQ and $P'Q$ are parallel to a pair of conjugate diameters.

Ex. 4.—Through a point P on an asymptote of a conic two lines PAB and PCD are drawn to meet the conic at A, B and C, D. Any conic through A, B, C, D meets this asymptote in U and V ; prove that P is the mid-point of UV.

Ex. 5.—P and Q are conjugate points with respect to a conic, and the mid-point of PQ lies on the conic; prove that PQ is parallel to an asymptote.

Ex. 6.—PP' is a diameter of a conic; the tangent at any point Q meets the tangent at P in T; $P'Q$ meets PT in R; prove that T is the mid-point of PR.

Ex. 7.—T is the pole of a chord PQ of a parabola; the diameter through T cuts the parabola in N, and PQ in V; prove that N is the mid-point of TV.

Ex. 8.—A variable tangent to a parabola cuts two fixed tangents in H and K; prove that the locus of the mid-point of HK is a line.

35. Foci and axes of a conic.—There are two pairs of tangents to a conic from I and J; these four lines define a complete quadrilateral, with pairs of opposite vertices, S, S'; H, H'; I, J. The four points S, S', H, H' are called the *foci* of the conic, and the lines SS', HH' the *axes* of the

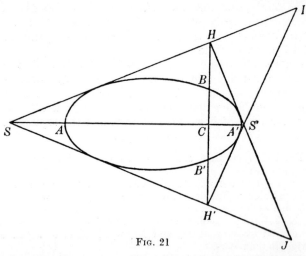

Fig. 21

conic. The diagonal triangle of the quadrilateral is formed by the lines SS', HH', IJ, and is a self-polar triangle with respect to the conic, and SS' meets HH' in the centre C,

the pole of *IJ*. Moreover, the lines *SCS'*, *HCH'* harmonically divide *CI* and *CJ*, and so *the axes are perpendicular
lines through the centre.*

The points of intersection of *SS'* and *HH'* with the conic
are usually denoted by *A*, *A'* and *B*, *B'* respectively. The
centre is evidently the mid-point of *AA'* and *BB'*.

The polars of the foci with respect to the conic are the
directrices. We will show that there are two directrices
parallel to each axis. The pole of *SS'* is the point of intersection of *HH'* and *IJ*, but, since the polars of *S* and *S'*
pass through this point, these lines are parallel to *HH'*.
The directrices corresponding to *S* and *S'* are thus parallel
to *HH'*, and similarly, the directrices corresponding to *H*
and *H'* are parallel to *SS'*.

The parabola.—The parabola touches the absolute line
IJ at its centre *C*. There is thus only *one focus S*, outside

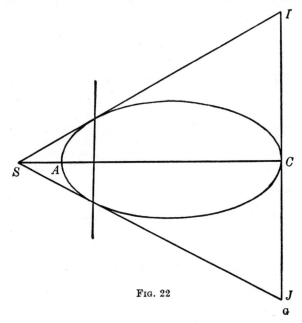

Fig. 22

the absolute line, for S' coincides with C and H, H' coincide with I, J. The parabola has *one axis*, the line which joins the focus to the centre C. The other point of intersection of the axis with the parabola is the *vertex A*. The polar of S is the directrix of the parabola, and the directrix is perpendicular to the axis.

Since there is only one conic which touches IJ and has double contact with CI and CJ at fixed points on these lines, it follows that there is a unique parabola with given focus and directrix.

Ex. 1.—Prove that the centre of a conic is the mid-point of the foci on either axis.

Ex. 2.—Prove that the axes of a conic are the unique pair of perpendicular conjugate diameters.

Ex. 3.—Prove that every pair of conjugate lines through a focus are perpendicular.

Ex. 4.—Prove that the projective properties of conics with a common focus and directrix are those of a system of concentric circles.

Ex. 5.—Prove that every conic through the four foci of a conic is a rectangular hyperbola.

Ex. 6.—Two conics have a common focus ; the directrices corresponding to this focus meet in P ; prove that one pair of their common chords also meet in P.

Ex. 7.—A pair of conjugate diameters of a conic, centre C, meet the directrix corresponding to a focus S in H and K ; prove that S is the orthocentre of the triangle CHK.

Ex. 8.—If a pencil of conics contain a circle, prove that the axes of the two parabolas it contains are perpendicular, and the axes of all conics of the pencil are in two fixed directions.

Ex. 9.—A is a fixed point and l a fixed line ; P is a variable point on l and the line PB is perpendicular to PA ; prove that the envelope of PB is a parabola with focus at A. (If PB meets the absolute line in P', then P and P' generate related ranges on l and the absolute line respectively.)

Ex. 10.—Through each point P of a line l is drawn the line p perpendicular to the polar of P with respect to a conic S. Show that the envelope of the lines p is a parabola which touches l.

Ex. 11.—One vertex F of a variable triangle MFN is fixed, and FM is perpendicular to FN, while the vertices M and N move on fixed lines TH and TK respectively. Prove that the envelope of MN is a conic of which F is a focus and which touches TH and TK.

Ex. 12.—O is a fixed point on a parabola. A variable line through O meets a fixed line l in X and the parabola again in Y. Prove that the envelope of a line through X parallel to the tangent at Y is another parabola. Find the common tangents of the two parabolas other than the absolute line, and determine the position of l if the parabolas have a common focus.

36. The director circle.—Let P be a point such that the tangents from P to a given conic are perpendicular. These tangents harmonically separate PI and PJ, and it follows, by **27**, that PI and PJ are conjugate lines with respect to the conic.

To find the locus of P we take any line through I; the conjugate line through J is obtained by joining J to the pole of this line with respect to the conic. There is thus a (1-1) correspondence between lines through I and the conjugate lines through J, and so the locus of P is a conic through I and J, that is, a circle; we have the theorem :

The locus of points from which the tangents to a conic are perpendicular is a circle.

This circle is called the *director circle* of the conic. We have seen, in **31**, that lines which pass through one of the absolute points are self-perpendicular, and so the points of intersection of the conic and its directrices lie on the director circle, for the tangents to the conic at these points pass through the absolute points.

The directrix of a parabola.—If the conic is a parabola the above result has to be modified. In this case the line IJ touches the conic, and the line conjugate to IJ is JI. Thus if P lies on IJ, then PI and PJ are conjugate lines, and so the line IJ is part of the locus. The remaining part of the locus is thus a line, and since it passes through the points of intersection of the parabola and its directrix, it must itself be the directrix. Moreover, as the focus and directrix are pole and polar, the chord of contact of tangents from a point on the directrix passes through the focus; thus:

Tangents at the ends of a focal chord of a parabola are perpendicular and meet on the directrix.

Ex. 1.—Prove that a conic and its director circle have the same centre.

Ex. 2.—What is the director circle of a rectangular hyperbola ?

Ex. 3.—Prove that the focus of a conic is a limiting point of the coaxal system having the corresponding directrix as radical axis, and the director circle as a circle of the system.

37. Confocal conics.—Confocal conics are conics with the same foci ; they form a pencil of conics inscribed to the quadrilateral defined by the two pairs of tangents from the absolute points to one conic of the system. Since there is a unique conic touching five lines, there is one conic of a confocal system which touches a given line.

By the dual of Desargues' theorem, the pairs of tangents from a point T to members of a confocal system form pairs of lines in involution. The double lines of the involution are tangents to the two members of the confocal system through T. Included in the involution are the pairs of lines joining T to the point pairs of the system S, S' ; H, H' ; I, J. The lines TI, TJ thus harmonically separate the tangents to the two confocals through T, and these tangents are therefore perpendicular ; we have the result :

Through any point there are two conics of a confocal system, and these two conics cut orthogonally.

We proved, in **29**, that the locus of the poles of a line with respect to conics inscribed to a quadrilateral is a line. If we take a line l, there is one conic of a confocal system which touches l, and let the point of contact be T. There are two confocals through T, and the poles of l with respect to these confocals are T, and some point lying on the tangent to the second confocal at T. Since this tangent is perpendicular to l, the locus of the poles of l with respect to conics of the confocal system is a line perpendicular to l through T. This line is called the normal at T to the confocal which touches l; hence:

The locus of the poles of a given line with respect to the conics of a confocal system is the normal at the point of contact to that confocal which touches the given line.

Confocal conics form a special case of conics touching four lines. We now obtain some of the properties of this more general system.

Conics inscribed to a quadrilateral.—Let us consider the director circles of the system of conics touching four lines; if two of these circles meet in T and T', then, included in the involution of pairs of tangents from T to conics of the system, there are two pairs which are perpendicular. The involution therefore consists of pairs of perpendicular lines, and so all pairs of tangents from T are perpendicular, and all the director circles pass through T and similarly through T'; we obtain the result:

The director circles of a pencil of conics inscribed in a quadrilateral form a coaxal system.

The radical axis of the coaxal system is evidently the directrix of the unique parabola of the system, and the point circles arise from the two rectangular hyperbolas of the system.

Included among the conics of the pencil are three point pairs, and the corresponding director circles are the circles with each of these point pairs as extremities of a diameter; therefore:

The three circles, whose diameters are the joins of opposite vertices of a quadrilateral are coaxal.

By **36**, Ex. 1, a conic and its director circle have the same centre, and moreover, the centres of circles of a coaxal system are collinear; hence:

The centres of all conics inscribed in a quadrilateral lie on the line containing the mid-points of the lines joining opposite vertices of the quadrilateral.

Ex. 1.—The envelope of the polars of a point with respect to a system of confocal conics is a parabola touching the axes of the conics.

Ex. 2.—From a fixed point O, lines are drawn to touch a conic belonging to a system of confocals in P and Q; show that PQ and the normals at P and Q touch a fixed parabola which touches the axes of the confocals.

Ex. 3.—The two conics which can be drawn touching four definite tangents of a given conic, and to pass through a particular focus of this conic have their tangents at this focus perpendicular.

Ex. 4.—The tangent and normal at a point P of a conic meet the axis SS' in T and G respectively; prove that (TG, SS') is harmonic.

Ex. 5.—Prove that parabolas with the same focus and axis form a line-pencil, and that any two parabolas of the pencil cut orthogonally.

38. The auxiliary circle.—If S is a focus of a conic, and I, J the absolute points, then SI and SJ are fixed tangents to the conic. Let a variable tangent cut SI in M and SJ in N. The points M and N then generate related ranges on SI and SJ respectively. Let JM meet IN in X and SX meet MN in Y.

By the harmonic theory of the quadrangle $SMXN$, the lines MN and SY meet the absolute line in points L, L' which harmonically separate I and J, and thus SY is perpendicular to MN. We will prove that the locus of Y is a circle.

By a further property of the quadrangle $SMXN$, the pencil of lines through J; JS, JM; JY and JI is harmonic, and, as JS and JI are fixed lines, it follows that, as M varies on SI, the lines JM and JY generate related pencils. Similarly IN and IY generate related pencils. Then, since M and N define related ranges on SI and SJ, it is evident

that the pencil of lines JY is related to the pencil of lines
IY, and the locus of Y is a conic through I and J, i.e. a
circle. If S lies on the axis AA' of the conic, we may show
that the circle has AA' as a diameter.

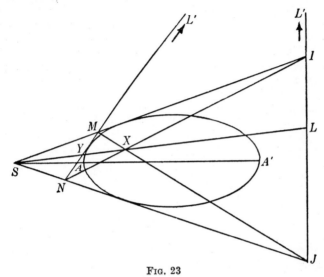

Fig. 23

The tangents at A and A' are perpendicular to SA and
SA' respectively, and so two positions of Y are at A and A',
and the locus passes through A and A'.

We show that the circle can meet the conic in no point
other than A and A'. Let P be a point of intersection of the
conic with the circle, and let SP meet IJ in R, and the
tangent at P meet IJ in Q. Since P lies on the circle, SP is
perpendicular to PQ, and so the pencil $S(QR, IJ)$ is harmonic, but, as SI, SJ are tangents, it follows that SR is
conjugate to SQ. Now the polar of S is the directrix, and
the polar of P is the tangent at P, and so these two lines
meet in the pole of SR. Since the pole of SR lies on SQ, it
follows that the directrix passes through Q. The point P

must therefore be one of the two points of contact of tangents from the point of intersection of the directrix, corresponding to the focus S, with the absolute line. These two points of contact are A and A'. Thus the only intersections of the circle and the conic are at A and A', and the circle has double contact with the conic at these points. Since the tangents at A and A' meet on the absolute line, it follows that the centre of the circle is on AA', and so the circle has AA' as diameter; we thus have the theorem:

The locus of the foot of the perpendicular from a focus upon a variable tangent to a conic is a circle which has as a diameter that axis of the conic which contains the focus.

The circle is called the *auxiliary circle* of the conic associated with the focus S. It is evidently associated in the same way with the other focus S' on AA'.

The parabola.—If the conic is a parabola the above proof needs modification. The pencil of lines JY is still related to the pencil of lines IY, but one of the tangents to the conic is the absolute line itself, and the position of Y corresponding to this tangent lies on IJ. The ray corresponding to JI of the pencil vertex J is thus IJ of the pencil vertex I, and the locus of Y degenerates into the tangent at the vertex of the parabola together with the absolute line; hence:

The locus of the foot of the perpendicular from the focus of a parabola upon a variable tangent is the tangent at the vertex of the parabola.

This is the converse of the result of **35**, Ex. 9.

39. Some properties of the parabola.—A parabola is a conic which touches the absolute line, and so parabolas which touch the three sides of a fixed triangle are inscribed to a quadrilateral and form a pencil. We obtain the locus of their foci.

If S is the focus of a parabola of the pencil the sides of the two triangles ABC and SIJ touch the parabola, and so, by **28**, their vertices lie on a conic ; this conic passes through I and J and is thus a circle ; therefore :

The circumcircle of a triangle which is circumscribed to a parabola passes through its focus.

This may be otherwise expressed :

The locus of the foci of parabolas inscribed to a triangle is the circumcircle of the triangle.

The three points A, B, C correspond to the three degenerate parabolas of the pencil.

Let H be the orthocentre of the triangle ABC and let the sides BC, CA, AB meet the absolute line in A', B', C' respectively. Since HA is perpendicular to BC, and since HA' is parallel to BC, it follows that HA is perpendicular to HA'. Similarly HB and HC are perpendicular to HB' and HC' respectively. The tangents from H to the parabolas of the pencil inscribed to the triangle ABC form pairs in involution, and the pairs HA, HA' ; HB, HB' ; HC, HC' are included in this involution, since the point pairs A, A' ; B, B' ; C, C' form the three degenerate parabolas of the pencil. Hence, pairs of tangents from H to a parabola of the pencil are perpendicular, and H lies on the directrix of the parabola. This result may be expressed :

The orthocentre of a triangle circumscribed to a parabola lies on the directrix, and the directrices of all parabolas inscribed to a triangle are concurrent.

40. Some properties of the rectangular hyperbola.

—A rectangular hyperbola is a conic which meets the absolute line in two points which harmonically separate the absolute points. Since perpendicular lines also meet the absolute line in two such points, they form a degenerate rectangular hyperbola.

We show that there is one rectangular hyperbola through four general points A, B, C, D. Conics through A, B, C, D form a pencil, and meet the absolute line in involution pairs. Let the double points be E, F. The two pairs E, F and I, J define another involution with double points X, Y. The pair

X, Y then harmonically separates E, F and thus belongs to the original involution, and it also harmonically separates I, J. The conic of the pencil through X, Y is thus a rectangular hyperbola, and is, in general, the only rectangular hyperbola through A, B, C, D.

Let us suppose that the pencil of conics through A, B, C, D is specialised in that it contains two rectangular hyperbolas. In this case two pairs of the involution defined by conics of the pencil on the absolute line harmonically separate the absolute points, and so all pairs of the involution harmonically separate I and J, and thus every conic of the pencil is a rectangular hyperbola. Included among the conics of the pencil are the line-pairs BC, AD; CA, BD; AB, CD. As these are all degenerate rectangular hyperbolas, they form pairs of perpendicular lines, and D is the orthocentre of the triangle ABC; we have the theorem :

Every conic through the four points of intersection of two rectangular hyperbolas is itself a rectangular hyperbola, and the four points form a triangle and its orthocentre.

Let us take any rectangular hyperbola circumscribing the triangle ABC, and let the perpendicular from A to BC meet the hyperbola in D; there are then two rectangular hyperbolas through D, the given hyperbola, and the line-pair BC, AD, and so, by the above, D is the orthocentre of the triangle ABC; hence :

If a rectangular hyperbola circumscribe a triangle ABC, it passes through its orthocentre.

Let us consider a system of parallel chords of a rectangular hyperbola ; they pass through a point H on the absolute line, and let K be the harmonic conjugate of H with respect to I and J. The two tangents from K to the curve are perpendicular to the system of parallel chords ; let their points of contact be P and P'. If QR is one chord of the system, there are two rectangular hyperbolas through the four points P, taken twice, Q and R, namely, the given hyperbola and the line-pair consisting of QR and the tangent at P. All conics through these points are thus rectangular hyperbolas, and, in particular, the line-

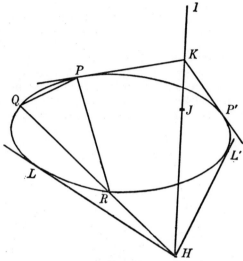

Fig. 24

pair PQ, PR forms a rectangular hyperbola, and so PQ is perpendicular to PR. A circle on QR as diameter thus passes through P and similarly through P'. The same result holds for all chords such as QR, and hence :

The circles described on parallel chords of a rectangular hyperbola as diameters are coaxal.

The limiting points of the coaxal system are the points of contact L, L' of tangents parallel to the system of parallel chords.

Ex. 1.—P, Q, R are points on a rectangular hyperbola, and PQ is perpendicular PR ; prove that the tangent at P is perpendicular to QR.

Ex. 2.—Prove that the circumcircle of a triangle which is self-polar with respect to a rectangular hyperbola passes through its centre. (If C is the centre of the hyperbola, the given triangle and the triangle CIJ are both self-polar with respect to the hyperbola, and their vertices lie on a conic, and since this conic contains I and J it is the circumcircle of the given triangle.)

Ex. 3.—The locus of the centres of rectangular hyperbolas for which a given triangle is a self-polar triangle is a circle.

41. The hyperbola of Apollonius.—Let O be a fixed point, and C the centre of a given conic. Let CP and CD be a pair of conjugate diameters, and let the line OQ be taken perpendicular to CP to meet CD in Q. It is evident that, as CP varies, there is a (1-1) correspondence between

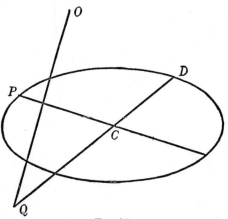

Fig. 25

CQ and OQ, for if OQ is known, CP, and therefore CQ, is uniquely determined, and similarly, if we know CQ, then CP, and consequently OQ, is defined. The locus of Q is therefore a conic through O and C. If CP is made to coincide with one of the axes of the conic, then the corresponding position of Q is the point of intersection of the other axis with the absolute line, and so the locus is a rectangular hyperbola with asymptotes parallel to the axes of the given conic. Moreover, if Q is a point of intersection of the locus with the given conic, then, since CQ is conjugate to CP, the tangent at Q is parallel to CP, and thus perpendicular to OQ. Therefore Q is the foot of one of the normals from O to the given conic. We thus have the theorem :

The feet of the normals which can be drawn from a fixed point to a conic lie on a rectangular hyperbola whose asymptotes are parallel to the axes of the conic.

The hyperbola is called the *hyperbola of Apollonius.* Since it meets the given conic in four points it follows that *four normals can be drawn from an arbitrary point to a conic.*

If the point O lies on one of the axes of the conic, the hyperbola of Apollonius contains three points on the axis OC, namely O, C and the point of intersection of OC with the absolute line, and thus degenerates into the axis OC together with another line, which, since the hyperbola is rectangular, is perpendicular to OC.

If the conic is a parabola the above proof needs modification. In this case C is the point of contact of the parabola with the absolute line. Let CD be a diameter, and let the line OQ be taken perpendicular to the tangent at D to meet CD in Q. Then, as D varies, there is, as above, a (1-1) correspondence between CQ and OQ, and the ocus of Q is a conic through O and C. If D coincides with C, the corresponding position of Q is the harmonic conjugate of C with respect to I and J. The locus of Q then meets the absolute line in points which harmonically separate the absolute points and is a rectangular hyperbola. The feet of the normals from O are the four intersections of this rectangular hyperbola with the parabola, but one of these points is C, and the normal at C is undefined. Thus, *there are three normals which may be drawn from an arbitrary point to a parabola.*

Ex. 1.—Prove that the hyperbola of Apollonius corresponding to a focus S consists of the axis which contains S and the directrix corresponding to S.

Ex. 2.—If the normal at O meets the conic again in N, prove that the pole of ON lies on the Apollonius hyperbola of O.

Ex. 3.—Prove that the point of intersection of OS with the directrix corresponding to a focus S lies on the Apollonius hyperbola of O.

Ex. 4.—P is any point on a parabola whose vertex is A, and Q, R are the feet of the normals from P to the curve. Show that QR passes through a fixed point and that AP and QR meet on a fixed line.

Ex. 5.—Prove that the feet of the normals from a point to a rectangular hyperbola form a triangle and its orthocentre.

42. The Frégier point.—Let O be a fixed point on a conic, and let PP' be a variable chord such that OP is perpendicular to OP'. Pairs of lines such as OP, OP' form pairs in involution, and P, P' define an involution of pairs of points on the conic. The lines PP' thus pass through a fixed point F, and since one particular position of PP' is the normal at O, the fixed point F lies on the normal at O; we have the result :

If O is a fixed point of a conic, and if PP' is a variable chord such that OP is perpendicular to OP', then PP' passes through a fixed point on the normal at O.

The point F is called the Frégier point of O.

Ex. 1.—Prove that the Frégier point of a point of a rectangular hyperbola lies on the absolute line.

Ex. 2.—Prove that for a parabola the mid-point of OF lies on the axis of the parabola.

CHAPTER V

THE EQUATION OF A LINE AND OF A CONIC: ALGEBRAIC CORRESPONDENCE ON A CONIC: THE HARMONIC LOCUS AND ENVELOPE

43. The equation of a line.—In 4 we proved that if we take three non-collinear points A, B, C as forming a triangle of reference, then any point P may be expressed in the form $P = xA + yB + zC$, where the numbers x, y, z are the coordinates of P.

If $P_1(x_1, y_1, z_1)$ and $P_2(x_2, y_2, z_2)$ are two points, any point $P(x, y, z)$ on the line $P_1 P_2$ may be written

$$P = \lambda P_1 + \mu P_2$$
$$= (\lambda x_1 + \mu x_2)A + (\lambda y_1 + \mu y_2)B + (\lambda z_1 + \mu z_2)C,$$

and so the coordinates of P are

$$x = \lambda x_1 + \mu x_2, \quad y = \lambda y_1 + \mu y_2, \quad z = \lambda z_1 + \mu z_2,$$

and eliminating λ and μ, we obtain

$$(y_1 z_2 - y_2 z_1)x + (z_1 x_2 - z_2 x_1)y + (x_1 y_2 - x_2 y_1)z = 0. \qquad (1)$$

The coordinates of any point upon the line $P_1 P_2$ thus satisfy a linear equation of the form

$$lx + my + nz = 0,$$

where l, m, n are constants.

Conversely, if l, m, n are given constants and $P_1(x_1, y_1, z_1)$ and $P_2(x_2, y_2, z_2)$ are any two points whose coordinates satisfy the equation $lx + my + nx = 0$, then

$$lx_1 + my_1 + nz_1 = 0 \text{ and } lx_2 + my_2 + nz_2 = 0,$$

and so $\qquad \lambda(lx_1 + my_1 + nz_1) + \mu(lx_2 + my_2 + nz_2) = 0,$

or $\qquad l(\lambda x_1 + \mu x_2) + m(\lambda y_1 + \mu y_2) + n(\lambda z_1 + \mu z_2) = 0$

for all values of λ and μ, and consequently all the points $(\lambda x_1 + \mu x_2, \ \lambda y_1 + \mu y_2, \ \lambda z_1 + \mu z_2)$, which are points of the line $P_1 P_2$, lie on the locus ; hence :

The equation of any line of the plane is of the form $lx + my + nz = 0$, where l, m, n are constants, and conversely, any equation of this form represents the points of a line.

The equation of the line joining the two points (x_1, y_1, z_1) and (x_2, y_2, z_2) is given by equation (1).

The coordinates of a line.—A line is thus determined by three constants l, m, n, and these constants are called the *coordinates of the line.* It is clear that the coordinates λl, λm, λn determine the same line as the coordinates l, m, n.

The equations of the sides BC, CA, AB of the triangle of reference ABC are $x = 0$, $y = 0$ and $z = 0$ respectively, and so the coordinates of these lines are $(1, 0, 0)$, $(0, 1, 0)$ and $(0, 0, 1)$ respectively.

Duality of point and line.—We may regard the equation $lx + my + nz = 0$ from two points of view. If we take l, m, n as constants, it represents all points (x, y, z) which lie upon the given line whose coordinates are (l, m, n). If instead, however, we take (x, y, z) as the coordinates of a fixed point, the equation represents all lines with co-ordinates (l, m, n) which pass through the fixed point (x, y, z). We may therefore speak of the equation $lx + my + nz = 0$ as representing in point-coordinates the equation of the line (l, m, n), and in line-coordinates the equation of the point (x, y, z). A line is thus represented by the general linear equation in the coordinates (x, y, z) of the points which lie on it, and dually, a point is represented by the general linear equation in the coordinates (l, m, n) of the lines which pass through it.

Ex. 1.—Prove that the coordinates of any line through the point of intersection of the lines whose coordinates are (l_1, m_1, n_1) and (l_2, m_2, n_2) are $(\lambda l_1 + \mu l_2, \ \lambda m_1 + \mu m_2, \ \lambda n_1 + \mu n_2)$.

Ex. 2.—Prove that the three lines whose coordinates are (l_1, m_1, n_1), (l_2, m_2, n_2) and (l_3, m_3, n_3) are concurrent if

$$l_1(m_2n_3 - m_3n_2) + m_1(n_2l_3 - n_3l_2) + n_1(l_2m_3 - l_3m_2) = 0.$$

Ex. 3.—Find the equation of the point of intersection of the lines whose coordinates are (l_1, m_1, n_1) and (l_2, m_2, n_2).

44. The equation of a conic.—In **21** we defined a conic as the locus of the meet of corresponding rays of two related pencils. If A and C are the vertices of the pencils, the conic passes through A and C; let the tangents at A and C meet in B. The rays AB, AC of the pencil vertex A then correspond to the rays CA, CB of the pencil vertex C. If P is a point of the conic, the rays AP and CP are related and meet BC and BA in U and V such that U and V describe related ranges on BC and BA respectively, and such that the points B and C on BC correspond to A and B on AB respectively. The point U may then be written $U = C + \theta B$, and the corresponding point $V = B + \phi A$, where $p\theta\phi + q\theta + r\phi + s = 0$. Since B and C on BC correspond to A and B on AB respectively it follows that when $\theta = \infty$, $\phi = \infty$, and when $\theta = 0$, $\phi = 0$. Hence $p = s = 0$, and the above relation connecting θ and ϕ reduces to $q\theta + r\phi = 0$. The unit point $A + B + C$ may be chosen arbitrarily. Let us take it as some point of the conic; then the values of U and V which arise when P is the unit point are $C + B$ and $B + A$ respectively, and so, when $\theta = 1$, $\phi = 1$; hence $q + r = 0$, the relation between θ and ϕ becomes $\theta - \phi = 0$ and $V = B + \theta A$. The point P, given as the intersection of AU and CV, is then represented by

$$P = \theta^2 A + \theta B + C.$$

The coordinates (x, y, z) of P, referred to ABC as triangle of reference are thus $x = \theta^2$, $y = \theta$, $z = 1$, and on elimination of θ, the equation of the conic is

$$y^2 - xz = 0.$$

We now refer the points of the plane to three other

H

fixed non-collinear points A', B', C' as triangle of reference ; we may then write,

$$A = a_1 A' + b_1 B' + c_1 C', \quad B = a_2 A' + b_2 B' + c_2 C',$$
and $$C = a_3 A' + b_3 B' + c_3 C',$$

where a_1, b_1, c_1, etc. are constants and so

$$P = \theta^2 (a_1 A' + b_1 B' + c_1 C') + \theta (a_2 A' + b_2 B' + c_2 C') + (a_3 A' + b_3 B' + c_3 C').$$

The coordinates (x', y', z') of P referred to the triangle $A'B'C'$ are thus

$$x' = a_1 \theta^2 + a_2 \theta + a_3, \quad y' = b_1 \theta^2 + b_2 \theta + b_3$$
and $$z' = c_1 \theta^2 + c_2 \theta + c_3.$$

Since the points A, B, C are not collinear, the determinant $|a_1 b_2 c_3| \neq 0$, and so we may deduce that

$$(\theta^2, \theta, 1) = (a_1' x' + b_1' y' + c_1' z', \quad a_2' x' + b_2' y' + c_2' z', \\ a_3' x' + b_3' y' + c_3' z'),$$

where a'_1, b'_1, c'_1 etc. are new constants depending on a_1, b_1, c_1 etc.

The coordinates (x', y', z') of P thus satisfy the equation

$$(a_1' x' + b_1' y' + c_1' z')(a_3' x' + b_3' y' + c_3' z') \\ - (a_2' x' + b_2' y' + c_2' z')^2 = 0,$$

which is of the second degree in the coordinates of P.

Conversely, we show that the general equation of the second degree

$$ax^2 + by^2 + cz^2 + 2fyz + 2gzx + 2hxy = 0$$

represents a conic.

If the left-hand side of this equation factorises, and the factors are $lx + my + nz$ and $l'x + m'y + n'z$, then the equation evidently represents the degenerate conic consisting of the pair of lines

$$lx + my + nz = 0 \quad \text{and} \quad l'x + m'y + n'z = 0.$$

If the left-hand side of the equation does not factorise,

we may take five points (x_1, y_1, z_1), (x_2, y_2, z_2), etc. on the locus, and we have

$$ax_1^2 + by_1^2 + cz_1^2 + 2fy_1z_1 + 2gz_1x_1 + 2hx_1y_1 = 0,$$

and four similar equations. We may solve these five equations and obtain unique values for the ratios of a, b, c, f, g, h in terms of x_1, y_1, z_1, etc.

Now there is a unique conic through these five points; let its equation be

$$a'x^2 + b'y^2 + c'z^2 + 2f'yz + 2g'zx + 2h'xy = 0.$$

Then $a'x_1^2 + b'y_1^2 + c'z_1^2 + 2f'y_1z_1 + 2g'z_1x_1 + 2h'x_1y_1 = 0,$

and four similar equations. It follows that the ratios of a', b', c', f', g', h' are then the same as those of a, b, c, f, g, h and so the equation

$$ax^2 + by^2 + cz^2 + 2fyz + 2gzx + 2hxy = 0$$

represents a conic.

Dually, we have the result that the lines which touch a conic have coordinates (l, m, n) which satisfy an equation of the form

$$Al^2 + Bm^2 + Cn^2 + 2Fmn + 2Gnl + 2Hlm = 0,*$$

and conversely, any equation of this form represents the lines which envelop a conic. This equation is called the line-equation of the conic.

Two conics meet in four points.—Let A and C be two points on one conic and let the tangents at these points meet in B; then referred to ABC as triangle of reference, general points of the two conics may be written

$$\theta^2 A + \theta B + C$$

and $(a_1\phi^2 + b_1\phi + c_1)A + (a_2\phi^2 + b_2\phi + c_2)B$
$$+ (a_3\phi^2 + b_3\phi + c_3)C,$$

where θ and ϕ are parameters defining points of the two

---

* We use the standard notation for the line-equation of a conic. The constants A, B, C in this equation are not to be confused with the points A, B, C.

conics, and $a_1, b_1, c_1, \ldots$ are constants. For a point common to both conics, the coefficients of A, B, C in the above expressions are proportional, and so

$$(a_2\phi^2 + b_2\phi + c_2)^2 = (a_1\phi^2 + b_1\phi + c_1)(a_3\phi^2 + b_3\phi + c_3) = 0,$$

and this is a quartic equation whose roots define the four points of intersection of the two conics.

Ex. 1.—If $S = 0$ and $S' = 0$ are the equations of two conics, prove that the equation $S + \lambda S' = 0$ represents a conic through their four points of intersection; dualise.

Ex. 2.—If $\Sigma = 0$ is the equation of a conic in line-coordinates, and if $\omega = 0$ and $\omega' = 0$ are the equations of the absolute points, prove that $\Sigma + \lambda\omega\omega' = 0$ represents, for different values of λ, conics confocal with $\Sigma = 0$.

Ex. 3.—Prove that, with suitable choice of triangle of reference, the equations of two conics with double contact may be written $y^2 - zx = 0$ and $y^2 - kzx = 0$.

Ex. 4.—Prove that the equations of two conics with three-point contact (three intersections coincident) may be written $y^2 - zx = 0$ and $y^2 - zx + \lambda zy = 0$.

Ex. 5.—Prove that the equations of two conics with four-point contact (all four intersections coincident) may be written $y^2 - zx = 0$ and $y^2 + \lambda z^2 - zx = 0$.

45. Tangent, pole and polar.—If $P_1(x_1, y_1, z_1)$ and $P_2(x_2, y_2, z_2)$ are two points, then any other point P on the line $P_1 P_2$ has coordinates $(\lambda x_2 + \mu x_1, \lambda y_2 + \mu y_1, \lambda z_2 + \mu z_1)$, and lies on the conic

$$f(x, y, z) \equiv ax^2 + by^2 + cz^2 + 2fyz + 2gzx + 2hxy = 0,$$

if
$$\begin{aligned} a(\lambda x_2 + \mu x_1)^2 &+ b(\lambda y_2 + \mu y_1)^2 + c(\lambda z_2 + \mu z_1)^2 \\ &+ 2f(\lambda y_2 + \mu y_1)(\lambda z_2 + \mu z_1) + 2g(\lambda z_2 + \mu z_1)(\lambda x_2 + \mu x_1) \\ &+ 2h(\lambda x_2 + \mu x_1)(\lambda y_2 + \mu y_1) = 0, \end{aligned}$$

or
$$\lambda^2 f_{22} + 2\lambda\mu f_{12} + \mu^2 f_{11} = 0, \qquad . \qquad . \quad (1)$$

where
$$\begin{aligned} f_{11} &= ax_1^2 + by_1^2 + cz_1^2 + 2fy_1z_1 + 2gz_1x_1 + 2hx_1y_1, \\ f_{12} &= (ax_1 + hy_1 + gz_1)x_2 + (hx_1 + by_1 + fz_1)y_2 \\ &\qquad + (gx_1 + fy_1 + cz_1)z_2, \\ f_{22} &= ax_2^2 + by_2^2 + cz_2^2 + 2fy_2z_2 + 2gz_2x_2 + 2hx_2y_2. \end{aligned}$$

(1) is a quadratic equation giving the ratio λ/μ, and it therefore determines those two points of the conic which lie on the line P_1P_2.

If the point $P_1(x_1, y_1, z_1)$ is on the conic, then $f_{11}=0$, and one of the values of λ/μ is zero. If, in addition, the line P_1P_2 is a tangent, the other value of λ/μ must be zero and $f_{12}=0$. The tangent at P_1 is then the locus of P_2, and its equation is

$$(ax_1 + hy_1 + gz_1)x + (hx_1 + by_1 + fz_1)y + (gx_1 + fy_1 + cz_1)z = 0.$$

Now let us suppose that P_1, P_2 are conjugate points with respect to the conic; then, if P_1P_2 meets the conic in P and P', the range (P_1P_2, PP') is harmonic. The co-ordinates of P and P' are then of the form $P(\lambda x_2 + \mu x_1, \lambda y_2 + \mu y_1, \lambda z_2 + \mu z_1)$ and $P'(\lambda x_2 - \mu x_1, \lambda y_2 - \mu y_1, \lambda z_2 - \mu z_1)$; the sum of the two values of λ/μ is zero, and $f_{12}=0$. The locus of P_2 is the polar of P_1, and its equation is thus

$$(ax_1 + hy_1 + gz_1)x + (hx_1 + by_1 + fz_1)y + (gx_1 + fy_1 + cz_1)z = 0.$$

46. The line-equation of a conic.—Let (x_1, y_1, z_1) be any point on the conic whose equation is

$$ax^2 + by^2 + cz^2 + 2fyz + 2gzx + 2hxy = 0,$$

and let us suppose the conic is non-degenerate. Then, by the result above, the tangent at (x_1, y_1, z_1) has the equation

$$(ax_1 + hy_1 + gz_1)x + (hx_1 + by_1 + fz_1)y + (gx_1 + fy_1 + cz_1)z = 0,$$

and its coordinates are thus (l, m, n),

where
$$ax_1 + hy_1 + gz_1 = kl,$$
$$hx_1 + by_1 + fz_1 = km,$$
$$gx_1 + fy_1 + cz_1 = kn.$$

Further, since the point (x_1, y_1, z_1) lies on the line (l, m, n), we have

$$lx_1 + my_1 + nz_1 = 0.$$

If we now eliminate x_1, y_1, z_1 and k from these last four equations we obtain

$$\begin{vmatrix} a & h & g & l \\ h & b & f & m \\ g & f & c & n \\ l & m & n & 0 \end{vmatrix} = 0,$$

and on expansion this becomes

$$Al^2 + Bm^2 + Cn^2 + 2Fmn + 2Gnl + 2Hlm = 0,$$

where A, B, C, F, G, H are the cofactors of a, b, c, f, g, h respectively in the determinant

$$\begin{vmatrix} a & h & g \\ h & b & f \\ g & f & c \end{vmatrix}.$$

We are thus able to write down the line-equation of a conic whose point-equation is given. A similar process enables us, dually, to obtain the point-equation of a conic where the line-equation is known.

Ex.—Write down the line-equations of the conics (i) $y^2 - zx = 0$, (ii) $ax^2 + by^2 + cz^2 = 0$, and (iii) $fyz + gzx + hxy = 0$.

47. Special forms for the equation of a conic.—The general equation of the second degree

$$ax^2 + by^2 + cz^2 + 2fyz + 2gzx + 2hxy = 0,$$

which represents a conic may be considerably simplified if the triangle of reference is suitably chosen. For example, if we choose three points A, B, C on the conic as vertices of the triangle of reference, it follows that the points $(1, 0, 0)$, $(0, 1, 0)$ and $(0, 0, 1)$ satisfy the equation of the conic, and so, $a = 0$, $b = 0$, $c = 0$. The equation of a conic which circumscribes the triangle of reference is then

$$fyz + gzx + hxy = 0.$$

Dually, the line-equation of a conic inscribed to the triangle of reference is

$$Fmn + Gnl + Hlm = 0.$$

Equation of a conic referred to a self-polar triangle.—Again, if we take as triangle of reference a triangle ABC, self-polar with respect to the conic, then the polar of A $(1, 0, 0)$ is BC, and its equation, which is $ax + hy + gz = 0$, reduces to $x = 0$, and so, $h = g = 0$. Similarly, $h = f = 0$ and $f = g = 0$. The equation of a conic referred to a self-polar triangle as triangle of reference is thus

$$ax^2 + by^2 + cz^2 = 0.$$

We proved, in **27**, that two conics meeting in four distinct points have a common self-polar triangle, which is the diagonal triangle of the quadrangle defined by the four points. If this common self-polar triangle is taken as triangle of reference, then the equations of the two conics can be written

$$ax^2 + by^2 + cz^2 = 0.$$

and $$a'x^2 + b'y^2 + c'z^2 = 0.$$

With suitable choice of unit point the first of these equations may be simplified still further. We make the transformation $x' = \sqrt{a}x$, $y' = \sqrt{b}y$, $z' = \sqrt{c}z$, a transformation under which the triangle of reference is unchanged, but the point which originally has coordinates

$$(1/\sqrt{a}, 1/\sqrt{b}, 1/\sqrt{c})$$

becomes the unit point. The above equations may then be written

$$x'^2 + y'^2 + z'^2 = 0,$$
$$a_1 x'^2 + b_1 y'^2 + c_1 z'^2 = 0,$$
where $$a_1 = a'/a, \; b_1 = b'/b, \; c_1 = c'/c.$$

This is usually the most convenient way of writing down the equations of two conics in general position.

Ex. 1.—Determine the line-equation of a conic (i), circumscribed to the triangle of reference, and (ii), with respect to which the triangle of reference is self-polar.

Ex. 2.—Determine the coordinates of the points common to $ax^2 + by^2 + cz^2 = 0$ and $a'x^2 + b'y^2 + c'z^2 = 0$.

48. Correspondence between points of a conic.— In **22** we discussed the general idea of related ranges on a conic. We suppose that the equation of the conic is $y^2 - xz = 0$, and the coordinates of the two points P and P' are $(\theta^2, \theta, 1)$ and $(\phi^2, \phi, 1)$ respectively. These points are related, or in (1-1) correspondence, if the parameters θ and ϕ are connected by the linear relation

$$p\theta\phi + q\theta + r\phi + s = 0.$$

If we take the double points of the correspondence to be the vertices A, C of the triangle of reference, then the equation $p\theta^2 + (q+r)\theta + s = 0$, giving the parameters of the double points, has roots $\theta = \infty$ and $\theta = 0$, and the above relation reduces to

$$q\theta + r\phi = 0.$$

The equation of the line PP' is

$$x - (\theta + \phi)y + \theta\phi z = 0,$$

and on substitution for ϕ

$$rx + (q - r)\theta y - q\theta^2 z = 0.$$

Its coordinates (l, m, n) are then

$$l = r, \quad m = (q - r)\theta, \quad n = -q\theta^2.$$

The envelope of PP' is thus the conic

$$qrm^2 + (q - r)^2 ln = 0,$$

and, if $q \neq r$, this conic is non-degenerate and has double contact with the given conic at A and C ; thus :

The envelope of the line which joins corresponding points of two related ranges on a conic is a conic having double contact with the given conic at the double points of the correspondence.

If $q = r$, the correspondence becomes an involution, and the envelope of PP' is the conic $m^2 = 0$, i.e. the point Y, taken twice.

The tangents at related pairs of points of a conic are also related, and so we obtain the following dual theorem :

The locus of the point of intersection of the tangents at corresponding points of two related ranges on a conic is a conic having double contact with the given conic at the double points of the correspondence.

Ex. 1.—Prove that the locus of the Frégier point of P, where P is a variable point of a given conic, is a conic with the same centre and asymptotes as the given conic.

Let PI, PJ meet the conic in Q, R respectively. Since PI is perpendicular to itself, the Frégier point of P lies on the tangent at Q, and similarly upon the tangent at R. It is thus the point of intersection F of these tangents. As P varies, Q and R generate related ranges on the conic, and the double points are the points of intersection of the conic with IJ. Thus, by the above theorem, the locus of F is a conic having double contact with the given conic at its points of intersection with IJ, i.e. a conic with the same centre and asymptotes as the given conic.

Ex. 2.—If two conics have double contact at X and Z, prove that a variable tangent to one conic cuts the other in pairs of corresponding points of two related ranges on the conic and X and Z are the double points of the correspondence.

Ex. 3.—A and B are two fixed points and P a variable point on a conic, and l is a fixed line cutting the conic in U and V; PA cuts l in R and BR cuts the conic in Q; find the envelope of PQ.

Ex. 4.—A variable triangle is inscribed in a given conic ; two of its sides are parallel to fixed lines ; prove that the envelope of the third side is a conic with asymptotes parallel to those of the given conic.

Ex. 5.—ABC is a fixed triangle inscribed in a given conic ; PQ is a variable chord such that $A(BC, PQ)$ is constant ; find the envelope of PQ.

Ex. 6.—If a polygon is inscribed in a conic, and all its sides but one pass through fixed points, prove that the envelope of that side is a conic having double contact with the given conic.

49. The symmetrical (2-2) correspondence of points on a conic.—In the last section we considered the most general linear relation connecting the parameters θ, ϕ of two points P and P' of the conic $y^2 - xz = 0$. This relation defined a (1-1) correspondence between P and P'. If θ and ϕ now satisfy an equation of the form

$$\theta^2(a\phi^2 + h_1\phi + g_1) + \theta(h_2\phi^2 + b\phi + f_1) + (g_2\phi^2 + f_2\phi + c) = 0,$$

then, given θ, we define two values of ϕ, and given ϕ, there arise two values of θ. This equation, which is the most general doubly quadratic expression in θ and ϕ, thus gives rise to a (2-2) correspondence between P and P', so that to every point P on the conic there correspond two points P' and to every point P' there correspond two points P.

We consider the special case when the correspondence is symmetrical and the fundamental relation reduces to

$$\theta^2(a\phi^2 + h\phi + g) + \theta(h\phi^2 + b\phi + f) + (g\phi^2 + f\phi + c) = 0. \quad (1)$$

In this case the two points corresponding to a given point of the conic are the same regardless of whether the point is taken as belonging to the range (P) or to the range (P'). The symmetrical (2-2) correspondence thus bears the same relation to the general (2-2) correspondence as the involution bears to the general (1-1) correspondence.

Since the relation depends on the five ratios of a, b, c, f, g, h, it is clear that a symmetrical (2-2) correspondence is completely defined when five pairs of corresponding points are given.

The equation (1) represents the condition for the point $P'(\phi^2, \phi, 1)$ to lie on the polar of $P(\theta^2, \theta, 1)$ with respect to the conic

$$ax^2 + by^2 + cz^2 + 2fyz + 2gzx + 2hxy = 0,$$

and so it is clear that any symmetrical (2-2) correspondence on a conic may be considered as defined by pairs of points of the conic conjugate with respect to another conic.

We will now find the envelope of PP' where P and P' are in symmetrical (2-2) correspondence on a conic.

If the equation of the conic is $y^2 - xz = 0$, then the co-ordinates of P and P' are $(\theta^2, \theta, 1)$ and $(\phi^2, \phi, 1)$ respectively, and the equation of the line PP' is

$$x - (\theta + \phi)y + \theta\phi z = 0,$$

and so, if its coordinates are (l, m, n), we have

$$l : m : n = 1 : -(\theta + \phi) : \theta\phi.$$

The equation (1) can, however, be written in the form

$$a\theta^2\phi^2 + h\theta\phi(\theta + \phi) + g[(\theta + \phi)^2 - 2\theta\phi] + b\theta\phi + f(\theta + \phi) + c = 0,$$

and so, on substitution for $(\theta + \phi)$ and $\theta\phi$,

$$an^2 - hmn + g(m^2 - 2ln) + bln - flm + cl^2 = 0,$$

which is the line-equation of a conic ; hence :

The envelope of the line joining corresponding points of a symmetrical (2-2) correspondence on a conic is another conic.

50. The harmonic envelope.—Let S and S' be two conics, and l a line which cuts S in a pair of points which harmonically separate its intersections with S'. We will prove that the envelope of l is a conic.

If l meets S in P and P', it is evident that P and P' are conjugate points with respect to S'. To construct a line l, we therefore take P as any point of S, and let the polar of P with respect to S' meet S in two points P' and P''. There are thus two points on S conjugate to P with respect to S'. Similarly, there are two points of S conjugate to P' with respect to S' and one of these points is P. There is thus a symmetrical (2-2) correspondence between P and P' and so the envelope of PP' is a conic.

Special members of the envelope arise if P is at any one of the four points of intersection of S and S', and in this case the members of the envelope through P are the tangents to both S and S' at this point ; hence :

The envelope of a line which is cut harmonically by two

conics S and S' is a conic which touches the eight tangents to S and S' at their four points of intersection.

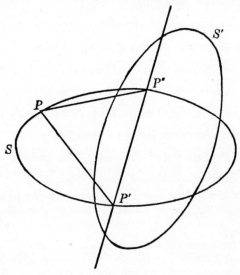

Fig. 26

This conic is called the *harmonic envelope* of S and S' and is usually denoted by Φ.

The harmonic locus.—The dual of the harmonic envelope is the *harmonic locus*; we have the result:

The locus of the point from which the pairs of tangents to two conics harmonically separate each other is a conic which passes through the eight points of contact of the common tangents of the two given conics.

The harmonic locus is usually denoted by **F**. If one of the given conics is a point-pair, the harmonic locus passes through these points and through the four points of contact of tangents from these points to the other conic. In particular, if one of the given conics consists of the absolute points I and J, the harmonic locus is the director circle of the other given conic.

Let two conics S and S' meet in the four distinct points A, B, C and D. The diagonal triangle XYZ of the quadrangle $ABCD$ is then the common self-polar triangle of the two conics. We will prove that it is also a self-polar triangle of the harmonic locus $\mathbf{F}$.

The four common tangents of the two conics form a quadrilateral for which XYZ is the diagonal triangle, and two common tangents PQ and $P'Q'$ meet in U on XZ. (See fig. 14 of 28.) One vertex of the diagonal triangle of the quadrangle $PQP'Q'$ is clearly U, and since U lies on the polar of Y with respect to either conic, the lines PP' and QQ' meet in Y, which is thus a second vertex of the diagonal triangle. If PQ' meets XZ in V, then, since Y is the pole of XZ with respect to either conic, the pencils $V(PP', XY)$ and $V(QQ', XY)$ are both harmonic, and as V, P, Q' are collinear, V, P', Q are also collinear, and the third vertex of the diagonal triangle is V. The triangle YUV is thus the diagonal triangle of the quadrangle $PQP'Q'$, and it is self-polar with respect to all conics through P, Q, P', Q'. Since the harmonic locus $\mathbf{F}$ passes through these points, the polar of Y with respect to $\mathbf{F}$ is UV, or XZ. Similarly, the polars of X and Z with respect to $\mathbf{F}$ are YZ and XY respectively, and so $\mathbf{F}$ has XYZ as a self-polar triangle.

Dually, we may show that the harmonic envelope Φ also has XYZ as a self-polar triangle ; hence :

Two conics S and S', which meet in four distinct points, their harmonic locus $\mathbf{F}$, and their harmonic envelope Φ, have a common self-polar triangle.

Ex. 1. — Prove that the harmonic locus of the conics $ax^2 + by^2 + cz^2 = 0$ and $x^2 + y^2 + z^2 = 0$ has the equation

$$a(b+c)x^2 + b(c+a)y^2 + c(a+b)z^2 = 0,$$

and the harmonic envelope has the line-equation

$$(b+c)l^2 + (c+a)m^2 + (a+b)n^2 = 0,$$

and hence show that these four conics have a common self-polar triangle.

Ex. 2.—Prove that the harmonic envelope of a circle and a rectangular hyperbola is a parabola.

Ex. 3.—Prove that the harmonic envelope of two ortho-gonal circles consists of their two centres.

Ex. 4.—What is the harmonic envelope of a parabola and a circle whose centre is at the vertex of the parabola ?

Ex. 5.—If the tangents to two conics at their four points of intersection are perpendicular, prove that, in general, these four points lie on a circle. (They lie on the director circle of the harmonic envelope.)

Ex. 6.—Prove that the harmonic envelope of two circles is a conic with one pair of foci at the centres of the circles.

Ex. 7.—If the conics S and S' have double contact at A and B, prove that both the harmonic locus and the harmonic envelope touch S and S' at A and B.

Ex. 8.—If S and S' have three-point contact at P, prove that the harmonic locus also has three-point contact with S and S' at P. If the harmonic locus cuts S and S' again in M and N respectively, and if S and S' meet again in L, prove that PM and PN are harmonic conjugates with respect to PL and the tangent at P.

51. A conic associated with three conics of a pencil. —In **29**, we defined a system of conics through four fixed points as belonging to a pencil. Let S, S', S'' be three conics of a pencil. We find the envelope of a line joining points of S and S' which are conjugate with respect to S''.

Let P and Q be points of S and S' respectively conjugate with respect to S'', and let the line PQ meet S, S', S'' in the three pairs of points P, P' ; Q, Q' ; R, R' respectively. Now, since P and Q are conjugate points with respect to S'', the range (PQ, RR') is harmonic. But, as the conics S, S', S'' belong to a pencil, the pairs P, P' ; Q, Q' ; R, R' are in involution, and so

$$(PQ, RR') = (P'Q', R'R),$$

and it follows that the range $(P'Q', R'R)$ is harmonic, and P', Q' are also conjugate with respect to S''.

Now, given P on S, there are two points of S' conjugate to P with respect to S'', and given by the intersections of S' with the polar of P with respect to S''. Thus, corresponding to P, there are two points such as Q, and hence two points such as P'. Moreover, if we choose P' on S, then, since $(P'Q', RR')$ is harmonic, its polar with respect to S'' meets S' in Q' and another point, and joining P' to these points and taking the intersections with S we derive P and another point. There is thus a symmetrical (2-2) correspondence between P and P' and the envelope of PP' is a conic, and so the envelope of PQ is a conic. We denote this conic by Ψ.

We now prove that the common tangents of S and S' are members of the envelope. Let a common tangent to S and S' touch them at A and B respectively. A and B

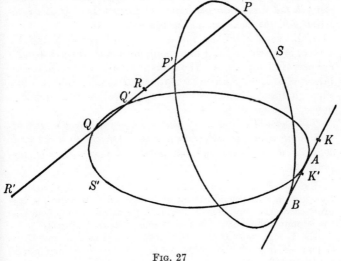

Fig. 27

are then the double points of the involution cut out on AB by conics of the pencil, and so A, B harmonically separate the points of intersection K, K' of AB with S''. A and B are thus conjugate points with respect to S'' and AB is a member of the envelope ; we have the theorem :

If S, S', S'' are three conics of a pencil, the envelope of a line joining a point P of S to Q of S' where P and Q are conjugate points with respect to S'' is a conic which touches the four common tangents of S and S'.

If S and S' coincide, Ψ is evidently the harmonic envelope of S and S''.

As a special case S'' may be a line-pair of the pencil defined by S and S', and if this is so, both lines are tangents to Ψ.

We have the dual theorem :

If $\Sigma, \Sigma', \Sigma''$ are conics of a line-pencil, then the locus of points of intersection of a tangent p of Σ' and q of Σ' such that p and q are conjugate lines with respect to Σ'' is a conic through the four common points of Σ and Σ'. If Σ'' is a point-pair, the locus passes through both points.

If Σ'' consists of the absolute points I and J, Σ and Σ' are confocal conics, and lines conjugate with respect to Σ'' are perpendicular lines. The locus of points of intersection of tangents to Σ perpendicular to tangents to Σ' is thus a conic through I and J and the four common points of Σ and Σ' ; hence :

The locus of the point of intersection of a variable tangent to a conic which is perpendicular to a tangent to a confocal conic is a circle through the points of intersection of the confocals.

Ex. 1.—P and Q are points of two circles S and S' respectively, such that the mid-point of PQ lies on their radical axis ; prove that the envelope of PQ is a parabola, which touches the common tangents of S and S' and their radical axis.

Ex. 2.—By taking Σ'' as the absolute points I, J and Σ' as a pair of foci of the conic Σ, deduce the auxiliary circle property of Σ.

CHAPTER VI

METRICAL GEOMETRY

52. Introduction.—In elementary geometry distance and angle are regarded as intuitive notions. Most of the theorems of Euclidean geometry, with which we were all familiar when at school, are concerned with the distance between points or the angle between lines, yet neither distance or angle is ever clearly defined. There are, however, certain fundamental properties which are tacitly assumed, and they can be summarised as follows.

If (PQ) denotes the distance between two points P and Q and (pq) the angle between two lines p and q, then :

   (i) $(PP) = 0$,
   (ii) $(PQ) = -(QP)$,
   (iii) If P, Q, R are three collinear points, then
   $(PQ) + (QR) = (PR)$,

and the corresponding properties for angles,

   (i) $(pp) = n\pi$, where n is an integer, positive, negative or zero.
   (ii) $(pq) = -(qp) + n\pi$,
   (iii) If p, q, r are three concurrent lines
   $(pq) + (qr) = (pr) + n\pi$.

It is therefore clearly desirable that in defining the terms distance and angle in projective geometry we should have regard to the above properties so fundamental in elementary geometry. We first of all give a general projective definition of distance and angle and later show how this definition may be modified to conform to the requirements of Euclidean geometry.

53. Projective definition of distance and angle.—
Let O and U be arbitrarily chosen fixed points on a line l,
and let P and Q be two other points upon the line. The
distance between P and Q is then defined by the expression

$$(PQ) = \frac{1}{2i} \log (PQ, OU).$$

Now it was proved, in **10**, that

$$(PQ, OU) \cdot (QR, OU) = (PR, OU)$$

or $\log (PQ, OU) + \log (QR, OU) = \log (PR, OU) + 2n\pi i$

(where n is an integer)*

and so $$(PQ) + (QR) = (PR) + n\pi.$$

Moreover, it is easily verified that

$$(PP) = n\pi \quad \text{and} \quad (PQ) = -(QP) + n\pi.$$

Thus, apart from the ambiguity arising because of the
periodicity of the logarithmic function, the projective
definition of distance fulfils the conditions stated in the
previous section.

We have thus defined distance upon a line in terms of
two fixed points on the line, and in a somewhat similar
manner we can define an angle at a point in terms of two
fixed lines through the point.

Let L be a fixed point and o, u two fixed arbitrarily
chosen lines through L, and let p, q be any other two lines
through L; the angle between p and q is then defined by
the expression

$$(pq) = \frac{1}{2i} \log (pq, ou).$$

54. The absolute conic.—We have now defined
distance on a line with regard to two fixed points O and
U of the line, and angle at a point with regard to two
fixed lines o and u through the point. The next step is

* Because the logarithmic function has period $2n\pi i$. Cf. Phillips:
Functions of a Complex Variable, p. 25.

to extend this definition and give a meaning to distance and angle in a plane.

Let us choose an arbitrary conic which we call the *absolute conic* and let us suppose, for the present, that this conic is non-degenerate. Any line PQ in the plane, not a tangent to the conic, meets it in two distinct points O and U, and we may use these points to define the distance between P and Q. Moreover, any two lines p and q meet in a point L, and from L there are two tangents o and u to the absolute conic. These two lines may then be used to define the angle between p and q; we then have the following formal definitions:

If we choose an arbitrary non-degenerate conic as the absolute conic, then (i), the distance between any two points P and Q is defined as any one of the values of $\frac{1}{2i} \log (PQ, OU)$, where O and U are the points of intersection of the line PQ with the absolute conic, and (ii), the angle between any two lines p and q is defined as any one of the values of $\frac{1}{2i} \log (pq, ou)$, where o and u are the two tangents to the absolute conic from the point of intersection of p and q.

A special case arises if either P or Q is on the absolute conic; the cross ratio (PQ, OU) is then either zero or infinite and the distance between P and Q is undefined. Similarly, if either p or q is a tangent to the absolute conic, the angle between p and q is undefined.

A further special case to be considered is when the line l joining two points P and Q touches the absolute conic. If this is so O and U coincide, the cross ratio $(PQ, OU) = 1$, and the distance between P and Q is $n\pi$, wherever P and Q may be on l. Dually, the angle between any two lines which intersect in a point of the absolute conic is equal to $n\pi$. The tangents and points of the absolute conic are called *isotropic lines* and *isotropic points* respectively.

It is evident from what has been said that distance in

projective geometry is not an inherent property of two points as in Euclidean geometry, but a property of these points in relation to an absolute conic. The absolute conic may be chosen in an arbitrary manner, and the distance between two points is obviously dependent upon this choice. Isotropic points and lines are not special in themselves, they are merely so because of some particular choice of the absolute conic.

Ex.—If P and Q are conjugate points with respect to the absolute conic, prove that the distance (PQ) is $n\pi + \pi/2$, and if p and q are conjugate lines with respect to the absolute conic, prove that the angle between p and q is $n\pi + \pi/2$. (Such points and lines are said to be *orthogonal*.)

55. Algebraic expressions for distance and angle.
—Let the equation of the absolute conic be $f(x, y, z) = 0$, and let the line PQ meet the conic in O and U. The points O and U may then be written

$$O = P + \lambda_1 Q \quad \text{and} \quad U = P + \lambda_2 Q,$$

and, if the coordinates of P and Q are (x_1, y_1, z_1) and (x_2, y_2, z_2) respectively, then, in the notation of **45**, the values of λ_1 and λ_2 are the roots of the equation

$$\lambda^2 f_{22} + 2\lambda f_{12} + f_{11} = 0. \qquad . \qquad . \qquad (1)$$

The parameters associated with the four points P, Q, O, U are $0, \infty, \lambda_1, \lambda_2$, and thus the value of the cross ratio

$$(PQ, OU)$$

is λ_1/λ_2, and so we may write

$$(PQ) = \frac{1}{2i} \log \lambda_1/\lambda_2.$$

This may be expressed

$$e^{2iPQ} = \lambda_1/\lambda_2$$

and so

$$\cos^2 (PQ) = \frac{1}{4}\left(e^{2iPQ} + 2 + e^{-2iPQ}\right)$$
$$= \frac{1}{4}\left(\frac{\lambda_1}{\lambda_2} + 2 + \frac{\lambda_2}{\lambda_1}\right).$$

Hence $$\cos^2 (PQ) = \frac{(\lambda_1 + \lambda_2)^2}{4\lambda_1\lambda_2},$$

and, using the expression for the sum and product of the roots of equation (1),

$$\cos^2 (PQ) = \frac{f_{12}^2}{f_{11}f_{22}}.$$

We have the theorem :

If the equation of the absolute conic is $f(x, y, z) = 0$, the distance between two points $P(x_1, y_1, z_1)$ and $Q(x_2, y_2, z_2)$ is given by

$$\cos^2 (PQ) = \frac{f_{12}^2}{f_{11}f_{22}},$$

and dually, if the line-equation of the absolute conic is $F(l, m, n) = 0$, the angle between the lines $p(l_1, m_1, n_1)$ and $q(l_2, m_2, n_2)$ is given by

$$\cos^2 (pq) = \frac{F_{12}^2}{F_{11}F_{22}}.$$

56. Real and complex points and lines.—Let us take three points A, B, C as triangle of reference, and $D = A + B + C$ as the unit point ; then any other point $P(x, y, z)$ of the plane may be written as $xA + yB + zC$. The point P is said to be a real point relative to A, B, C and D if the ratios of the coordinates x, y, z are all real numbers.

A point such as $(i, 2i, 3i)$ is represented as $(1, 2, 3)$ and is thus real.

All points which are not real are called complex points.

Now to identify, in a rigorous manner, the real points defined above with the real points of elementary geometry is beyond the scope of this book. To do so would involve a detailed discussion of the notions of *order* and *continuity*. We can here do no more than make a general statement, and refer the reader to Robinson, *Foundations of Geometry*,

Chapters V, VI and VII, or to Baker, *Principles of Geometry*, Vol. I, Chapter II, for a thorough analysis.

It is clear that, if A, B, C, D are four general points in a plane, we can construct the three diagonal points X, Y, Z of the quadrangle $ABCD$. From the seven points now given, we can obtain further points as the intersections of lines got by joining pairs of these seven points. Proceeding in this manner we can evidently obtain a very large number of points of the plane. If the original points A, B, C, D are real, all these points are given by a real construction, and we may show, by using the symbolic methods of Chapter I, that each one may be expressed in the form $xA + yB + zC$, where x, y, z are real. We are thus led to assume that there is an exact correspondence between the totality of real points of the plane and the ratios of the real numbers x, y, z such that every real point can be expressed in the form $xA + yB + zC$, and such that to every set of real values of x, y, z there corresponds a real point.

Dually, we may define a real line by means of three real coordinates l, m, n and any other line is called a complex line.

Ex. 1.—Prove that a line with two real points contains an infinite number of other real points.

Ex. 2.—Prove that every line, whether real or complex, contains complex points.

Ex. 3.—Prove that through a complex point there passes one and only one real line.

Ex. 4.—Prove that the real line through the complex point $P(x_1 + ix_2, y_1 + iy_2, z_1 + iz_2)$ also contains the point $P'(x_1 - ix_2, y_1 - iy_2, z_1 - iz_2)$. P and P' are called *conjugate complex points*).

Ex. 5.—What are the duals of the theorems of Ex. 3 and Ex. 4.

57. Real and complex conics.—A real conic is defined as a conic whose equation has real coefficients and which contains at least one real point. It is easy to show that if such a conic is non-degenerate it contains an infinite number of real points.

A real line meets the conic in points whose coordinates depend ultimately upon the solution of a quadratic equation with real coefficients, and, if one root of this equation is real, so must be the other. Thus if one point has real coordinates so has the other and the second point is also real. By taking an infinite number of real lines through the one real point of the conic we thus get an infinite number of real points on the conic, one on each line.

The only exceptional case is when the conic is degenerate, and consists of two complex lines meeting in the real point.

As examples of real and complex conics, we may consider those whose equations are

$$-x^2 + y^2 + z^2 = 0 \qquad . \qquad . \qquad . \quad (1)$$

and
$$x^2 + y^2 + z^2 = 0. \qquad . \qquad . \qquad . \quad (2)$$

The first conic obviously contains an infinite number of real points of the form $(\sqrt{(y_1{}^2 + z_1{}^2)}, y_1, z_1)$, given for all y_1, z_1, while the second conic clearly has no real point.

58. Metrical geometry.—Metrical geometry is the geometry which arises when properties involving distance or angle are considered. In **54** we defined distance and angle by means of an absolute conic, and so, since in metrical geometry, we are primarily concerned with the real points of the plane, we must make a distinction between the cases when the absolute conic is real and when it is complex.

If the absolute conic is real the resulting metrical geometry is *hyperbolic geometry*. On the other hand if the absolute conic is complex, but given by an equation with real coefficients, the resulting geometry is *elliptic geometry*. For example, the conics given by equations (1) and (2) of **57**, if taken as absolute conics, give rise to hyperbolic and elliptic geometries respectively.

The metrical theorems which define the relationship between the real points of the plane and the absolute conic are, as we should expect, different in these two geometries. For example, if we define parallel lines as lines which meet on the absolute conic, it may be proved that in hyperbolic geometry there are two lines through a given point parallel to a given line, but in elliptic geometry there is no line through a given point parallel to a given line.

In the next section we are concerned with a particular form of metrical geometry which arises when the absolute conic is degenerate and consists of two complex points. This geometry is a limiting case of the more general metrical geometry, and can be regarded as filling the borderline position between hyperbolic and elliptic geometry. In the particular case when the absolute conic is identified with the so-called circular points at infinity of elementary geometry the geometry arising is Euclidean.

59. Distance and angle in Euclidean geometry.—
We take as absolute conic the conic whose equation is

$$k(x^2 + y^2) + z^2 = 0.$$

The line-equation of this conic is

$$l^2 + m^2 + kn^2 = 0.$$

If k is positive, the conic is complex, and the geometry we obtain is elliptic, and if k is negative, the conic is real and the geometry is hyperbolic. We consider the limiting case when $k = 0$. The point-equation of the conic is then $z^2 = 0$, and it represents the line whose coordinates are $(0, 0, 1)$, taken twice. The line-equation of the conic reduces to $l^2 + m^2 = 0$, and represents the pair of points whose coordinates are $(1, i, 0)$ and $(1, -i, 0)$. These points we denote by I and J, and they are called the absolute points.

Angle between two lines.—The angle between two lines p and q through a point L is defined as

$$(pq) = \frac{1}{2i} \log \, (pq, \, ou)$$

where o and u are the lines joining L to the absolute points I and J. This definition is clearly equivalent to that given in **54**, for the lines o and u can be regarded as tangents to the absolute conic.

If p and q are conjugate lines with respect to I and J, the cross ratio $(pq, \, ou) = -1$, and $(pq) = n\pi + \pi/2$, where n is an integer. The angle between two perpendicular lines is thus, apart from a periodic term, $\pi/2$.

Let us take two lines p and q with coordinates (l_1, m_1, n_1) and (l_2, m_2, n_2) respectively, and the equation of the absolute conic as

$$F(l, m, n) \equiv l^2 + m^2 + kn^2 = 0.$$

The angle between the lines is given by the result quoted in **55**, and we have

$$\cos^2 \, (pq) = \frac{F_{12}{}^2}{F_{11} F_{22}},$$

and if k tends to zero this becomes

$$\cos^2 \, (pq) = \frac{(l_1 l_2 + m_1 m_2)^2}{(l_1{}^2 + m_1{}^2)(l_2{}^2 + m_2{}^2)},$$

and owing to the identity

$$(l_1 l_2 + m_1 m_2)^2 + (l_1 m_2 - l_2 m_1)^2 = (l_1{}^2 + m_1{}^2)(l_2{}^2 + m_2{}^2)$$

we obtain

$$\sin^2 \, (pq) = \frac{(l_1 m_2 - l_2 m_1)^2}{(l_1{}^2 + m_1{}^2)(l_2{}^2 + m_2{}^2)},$$

and so, if no regard be paid to sign,

$$\cos \, (pq) = \frac{(l_1 l_2 + m_1 m_2)}{\sqrt{(l_1{}^2 + m_1{}^2)} \sqrt{(l_2{}^2 + m_2{}^2)}}$$

and
$$\sin (pq) = \frac{(l_1 m_2 - l_2 m_1)}{\sqrt{(l_1{}^2 + m_1{}^2)} \sqrt{(l_2{}^2 + m_2{}^2)}}.$$

These expressions thus give the angle between two lines whose coordinates are known.

Distance between two points.—Since the absolute conic reduces to $z^2 = 0$ when $k = 0$, a line PQ meets the absolute conic in two coincident points. The distance (PQ), depending as it does on the cross ratio of four points, two of which are coincident, is thus undefined, and can only be obtained as the result of a limiting process.

Let the points P and Q have coordinates (x_1, y_1, z_1) and (x_2, y_2, z_2) respectively, and let us take the equation of the absolute conic as

$$f(x, y, z) \equiv k(x^2 + y^2) + z^2 = 0,$$

where we suppose k tends to zero.

By the result of **55**, the distance between P and Q is given by

$$\cos^2 (PQ) = \frac{f_{12}{}^2}{f_{11} f_{22}},$$

and so
$$\sin^2 (PQ) = \frac{f_{11} f_{22} - f_{12}{}^2}{f_{11} f_{22}},$$

substituting

$$f_{11} = k(x_1{}^2 + y_1{}^2) + z_1{}^2,$$
$$f_{22} = k(x_2{}^2 + y_2{}^2) + z_2{}^2,$$

and
$$f_{12} = k(x_1 x_2 + y_1 y_2) + z_1 z_2,$$

we obtain

$$\sin^2 (PQ) = \frac{k(z_1 x_2 - z_2 x_1)^2 + k(z_1 y_2 - z_2 y_1)^2 + k^2 U}{z_1{}^2 z_2{}^2 + kV + k^2 W},$$

where U, V, W are polynomials not involving k.

Therefore

$$\lim_{\to 0} \frac{\sin^2 (PQ)}{k} = \frac{(z_1 x_2 - z_2 x_1)^2 + (z_1 y_2 - z_2 y_1)^2}{z_1{}^2 z_2{}^2}.$$

Now if we assume that neither P or Q lie on the absolute line, then z_1 and z_2 are non-zero quantities, and so $\sin(PQ)$ approaches zero but in such a way that $\dfrac{\sin(PQ)}{\sqrt{k}}$ approaches a definite limit. Let us write therefore

$$d = \lim_{k \to 0} \frac{\sin(PQ)}{\sqrt{k}} = \lim_{k \to 0} \frac{(PQ)}{\sqrt{k}},$$

and we have

$$d^2 = \frac{(z_1 x_2 - z_2 x_1)^2 + (z_1 y_2 - z_2 y_1)^2}{z_1^2 z_2^2}.$$

Since we have supposed that neither P nor Q lies on the absolute line $z = 0$, we may put $z_1 = z_2 = 1$, and we finally obtain

$$d^2 = (x_2 - x_1)^2 + (y_2 - y_1)^2,$$

which is the well-known formula for the distance between two points in Euclidean geometry.

We may thus regard Euclidean geometry as a metrical geometry where the absolute conic is degenerate and consists of two distinct points I and J, and where the coordinate system is so arranged that I and J have the coordinates $(1, i, 0)$ and $(1, -i, 0)$ respectively. The angle between two lines and the distance between two points are then given by the formulae quoted above.

If XYZ is the triangle of reference, and if the absolute points I, J have coordinates $(1, i, 0)$ and $(1, -i, 0)$ respectively, then we have $I = X + iY$ and $J = X - iY$ and I, J harmonically separate X, Y and so ZX is perpendicular to ZY. The choice of the coordinates $(1, i, 0)$ and $(1, -i, 0)$ for I and J respectively is thus equivalent to taking a triangle of reference consisting of two perpendicular lines together with the absolute line. The two perpendicular lines meet in Z, and Z is usually called the *origin*.

Further, if any point P is given by $P = x_1 X + y_1 Y + Z$, and if PY meets ZX in M, then $M = x_1 X + Z$ and M has coordinates $(x_1, 0, 1)$. Since Z is the point $(0, 0, 1)$, it follows, by use of the above distance formula, that $(ZM) = x_1$ and

$(MP) = y_1$, and moreover MP is perpendicular to ZX; x_1, y_1 are thus the *rectangular cartesian coordinates* of the point P.

60. The Euclidean equivalents of simple projective elements.

—The various projective elements, which have been defined earlier, have their counterparts in Euclidean geometry. For example, we have already shown that the projective concept of perpendicular lines, as lines which meet the absolute line in points which harmonically separate the absolute points, corresponds in Euclidean geometry to the idea of lines which meet at an angle of $\pi/2$. We establish below other equivalent definitions.

The mid–point of a line.—Let P and Q have co-ordinates $(x_1, y_1, 1)$ and $(x_2, y_2, 1)$ respectively. The point of intersection of PQ with the absolute line $z = 0$ has co-ordinates $(x_2 - x_1, y_2 - y_1, 0)$, and so the harmonic conjugate of this point with respect to P and Q has coordinates

$$(x_2 + x_1, y_2 + y_1, 2) \quad \text{or} \quad \left(\frac{x_2 + x_1}{2}, \frac{y_2 + y_1}{2}, 1 \right).$$

This point is, by **31**, the mid-point M of PQ. We may now easily verify, by using the distance formula of **59**, that the distances (PM) and (MQ) are equal. This establishes the equivalence of the projective and Euclidean definitions of the mid-point.

The bisector of an angle.—Let l and m be two lines meeting in O and let them meet the absolute line in L and M respectively. The two pairs of points I, J and L, M determine an involution on IJ, and let the double points of the involution be X and Y. The lines OX and OY are then the unique pair of perpendicular lines which harmonically separate l and m, and they are called the *bisectors of the angles* between l and m.

To justify this definition, we notice that the points corresponding to L, X, I, J of the above involution on the absolute line are M, X, J, I respectively, and so

$$(LX, IJ) = (MX, JI)$$
$$= (XM, IJ).$$

Thus the angle between l and x is equal to the angle between x and m, and similarly the angle between l and y is equal to the angle between y and m. This establishes the equivalence of the projective and Euclidean definitions of the angle bisectors.

The circle.—A circle is a conic through I and J. Let the coordinate system be so chosen that the centre C of the circle is the point $(0, 0, 1)$ and I, J are the points $(1, i, 0)$ and $(1, -i, 0)$ respectively. The lines CI and CJ then have the equations $x + iy = 0$, and $x - iy = 0$ respectively, and they touch the circle at I and J respectively. The equation of the circle is thus of the form

$$(x + iy)(x - iy) - kz^2 = 0,$$

or, putting $z = 1$,

$$x^2 + y^2 - k = 0.$$

Any point $(x, y, 1)$ on the circle is thus at a constant distance $\sqrt{k}$ from the centre $(0, 0, 1)$, which gives us the Euclidean definition of a circle.

Ex. 1.—A rhombus is defined as a quadrilateral with two sides of its diagonal triangle perpendicular, and the third side coincident with the absolute line; prove that (i) the sides are equal in length, and (ii) the diagonals bisect one another.

Ex. 2.—If the absolute points have coordinates $(1, i, 0)$ and $(1, -i, 0)$, obtain the coordinates of the foci of the conic $ax^2 + by^2 + cz^2 = 0$, and show that, if a, b, c are real, two are real and two complex.

Ex. 3.—Prove that the conic of Ex. 2 is a rectangular hyperbola if $a + b = 0$, and show that its asymptotes have the equations $x + y = 0$ and $x - y = 0$.

Ex. 4.—If the absolute points have coordinates $(1, i, 0)$ and $(1, -i, 0)$, prove that the conic $y^2 - zx = 0$ is a parabola; find its focus and directrix.

INDEX

The numbers refer to the pages